AN INTRODUCTION TO ENGINEERING

Chinyere Onwubiko
Professor and Head
Mechanical Engineering Department
Tennessee State University

Schroff Development Corporation
ISBN 1-887503-34-X

An Introduction to Engineering

First edition, June 1996
Printed in the United States of America
ISBN: 1-887503-34-X
Published by Schroff Development Corporation, Mission, Kansas

CONTENTS

v

Chapter 15   Assembly

Introduction   253
15.2 Assembly Process 253
15.3 Assembly Systems   254
15.4 Design For Assembly Principles   255
    Rules For Design For Assembly   256
    Applying Design For Assembly Principles   259

    UNIT CONVERSIONS   **264**

  B.   **TRIGONOMETRY REVIEW**   **265**

  C.   **GEOMETRY REVIEW**   **269**

  D.   **QUICK BASIC RESERVED WORDS**   **273**

  E.   **GENERAL INFORMATION**   **275**

  F.   **GOLDEN-SECTION PROGRAM**   **277**

    ANSWERS TO SELECTED PROBLEMS   **279**

    INDEX   **281**

PREFACE

Engineering educators face an enormous challenge in preparing engineers for the 21st century. They have to do this in the midst of various obstacles. Some of these include a decline of interest in engineering, students with little knowledge of how things work, low enrollment, and low student retention rate. As a result, a great emphasis is placed on the freshman engineering course designed to introduce the freshman to the engineering profession. There are at least two main approaches to this course. The **traditional approach** simply introduces the fundamentals of engineering. Typically, this is done generally, in a disjoint manner so that the student sees no real connection between these various topics that are covered. The most recent approach is the "**Project driven**" method. The essence of this approach is to introduce engineering topics as they are needed while carrying out design projects that students are assigned.

This book proposes an approach that allows the student to understand the connection between the various engineering topics covered in some of these courses. Thus this book can be effectively used by individuals following either approach to a freshman engineering course. The main thrust of the book is to constantly remind the student that engineering design is a process driven by a lot of decision making that is based on different kinds of information.

The book is divided into three sections. Each section contains an introduction that describes why the section is important in the engineering profession. Chapters 1 through 4 comprise the first section . This section deals with introductory concepts in engineering and problem solving methodologies. The second section, consisting of Chapters 5 to 13, covers the essential phases of engineering design. This section also covers decision making tools and tools used for engineering design. The final section is an introduction to manufacturing processes and consists of Chapters 14 and 15.

The personal pronoun "he" is used throughout this text. This term is used to make the text more readable. The author wants all students, male and female, to become successful engineers.

TO THE INSTRUCTOR

The materials presented in the book can be covered in a three-hour credit semester course. To do this, the first three Chapters should be covered in rapid fashion. A significant amount of time should be spent on the methodologies presented in Chapter 4. Depending on the approach chosen, design projects may be assigned at the end of the fourth chapter before actually introducing the students to the design process in Chapter 5. Considerable time should be spent on Chapter 5. Chapter 6 provides the opportunity to apply the methodology covered in Chapter 4. Chapter 8 may be skipped without any significant disruption to the flow of the course. Although most incoming freshmen may already have an appreciable knowledge of word processing and spreadsheets, Chapter 9 should be carefully handled since the contents are designed to re-enforce the design process.

Special Request   It is difficult to catch every error. I am therefore requesting that any error noted or any suggestion of how to improve the second edition should be communicated to me at Department of Mechanical Engineering, Tennessee State University, 3500 John A. Merritt Blvd., Nashville , TN. Your communication will be acknowledged.
C.O.O.

ACKNOWLEDGMENTS

I am indebted to Dr. Decatur B. Rogers, my Dean, under whose directives I became interested in teaching an Introduction to Engineering Course which resulted in the writing of this book.

I am grateful to many of my reviewers for their critical suggestions especially Dr. Larry Richards, Director, Center for Computer Aided Engineering, University of Virginia. The comments and the editorial help provided by Dr. Landon Onyebueke and Prof. Ida McClain of Tennessee State University are appreciated.

My acquiring editor, Mr. Stephen Schroff and his staff at the Schroff Development Corporation deserve special thanks. My colleagues Dr. F.Mishu, Dr. S. Devgan, Prof. W. Vincent and Dr. M. Malkani who have contributed immensely in the development of an Introduction to Engineering course at Tennessee State University deserve special recognition.

Many more individuals, such as Mrs. Francis Delcau, my former secretary, deserve to be acknowledged than space permits. Ngozi, Chinwendu, Udochi, and Amarachi, for the special way they have helped during the writing of this book, I say "thanks a million times !!!."

SECTION 1

INTRODUCTORY CONCEPTS IN ENGINEERING

An engineer at work

Section One consists of four chapters that deal with
introductory materials. Chapter 1 gives a cursory overview of
the history of contributions to the engineering profession by
various individuals and nations.   The various engineering
disciplines and the activities of each discipline are presented in
Chapter 2. The engineering profession, typical engineering
curriculum, ethics and the essence of successful engineering
student are discussed in Chapter 3. Perhaps the most important
chapter is Chapter 4. This is because the student is introduced
to units and the scientific approach to problem solving. This
chapter must be carefully covered because it is important for
the beginning student to develop a mind set of how to solve
scientific problems in general but more specifically, the
engineering problems.

NOTES

CHAPTER 1

HISTORY OF ENGINEERING

1.1 EGYPTIAN ENGINEERS

Engineering designs and inventions are generally driven by human needs. It may be argued that the real engineering activities of Egypt were driven by a belief in life after death. This belief led the kings to build tombs they believed would contain all that they needed to make them happy in the life after death. The tombs were first built from burnt bricks, and later stones. Therefore, the first known engineering activity of Egypt is that of building. From available information, the first significant engineering work of Egypt was the building of the wall of the City of Memphis, a city which was the then capital of the Old Egyptian Kingdom.

Egypt produced many ancient engineers who were primarily architects. The first known engineer was Imhotep, who built the first pyramid for King Joser. History reveals that the structure of the pyramid came as a result of Kings changing their minds about what they wanted, attesting strongly to the fact that engineering design involves many decisions and revisions of original ideas and concepts. Pyramids were also built by the powerful Kushite Kings who lived in the area corresponding to the modern Sudan. The Egyptian engineers constructed canals, mostly for irrigation purposes, and dams.

Examination of these building projects in Egypt provides insight into how the ancient engineers solved problems. Since some of the pyramids reached a height of 480 feet, one cannot help but wonder how they were able to move the heavy stones that were used, bearing in mind that they did not have cranes and fork lifts. Historians and archaeologists have indicated that they used earthen mounds and ramps for hauling these stones to such heights. To the modern mind these may sound like simple solutions, but for these first engineers such solutions were quite innovative.

Another aspect of these endeavors is a consideration of what these early engineers contributed to the modern society. Through building projects, they learned much about quarrying, moving heavy stones and shaping them which no doubt contributed to many of today's technological advances.

1.2 MESOPOTAMIAN ENGINEERS

Mesopotamia is the name given to the land between the two rivers, Euphrates and Tigris, which is the location of modern Iraq. In the previous section we alluded to the building of canals by the Egyptian engineers. Actually, history indicates that the first canals were built by the Sumerians who lived in southern Mesopotamia. These canals were built for irrigation purposes. The desert-like condition of the land of Mesopotamia led to canal construction. Because of the need to irrigate, the Mesopotamia engineers made the first advances in bucket hoist for lifting water. The first use of pulleys, which made it easier to draw water from wells, is also attributed to the Mesopotamia engineers.

Like the Egyptian engineers, the Mesopotamia engineers also built walls and houses. These houses had doors similar in concept to the modern doors. To support these doors they used vertical pins at the hinge corners. The bottom pin was placed in a stone door socket while the upper pin was clutched in place by a strap. There were other engineering advances attributed to the Mesopotamia engineers but these advances are traceable to the Assyrians who captured Mesopotamia. The Assyrians were noted for their fierce military machines. They were the first to equip their soldiers with iron weapons. They developed new wheeled war machines and wagons. The modern day four-wheeled vehicle owes its beginning to the efforts of the Assyrian-Mesopotamia engineers. Other significant contributions of the Assyrians were made by their King-Engineer, Sennacherib, who built an aqueduct and paved streets. Further contribution of the Mesopotamia engineers include the building of the oldest known stone bridge attributed to the Chaldeans.

1.3 GREEK ENGINEERS

The Greek engineering efforts paralleled those of Egypt and Mesopotamia since some of their engineering concepts in building structures were borrowed from them. However, they were able to advance quickly with the borrowed concepts. The first known use of metal structural members in building was introduced by the Greek architects. It is believed that the first connection between pure science and engineering was introduced by the Greeks. For example, Archytas of Taras, during the Greek Golden Age was considered both a pure scientist and an engineer. He solved a number of mathematics and mechanics problems. As an engineer, he invented the mechanical bird that flew by compressed air. The invention of the screw is also attributed to him by some technology historians.

The Greek engineers were involved in other projects such as drainage and tunnels. However, they were unsuccessful in digging a canal across the Isthmus of Corinth. Another invention of the Greek engineers was the catapult used as one of the effective means of artillery in sea warfare.

Further contributions of Greek engineers took place under the Hellenistic Greeks, a mixture of Greeks and Orientals, which was an arrangement attributed to Alexander the Great. One of the outstanding contributions of this period is the writing of the book called "Mechanics." Historians do not agree as to the author of this master piece but its contents definitely contributed to some of the mechanical devices of our present time. For example, the description of "gear trains" found in it may have given rise to the advances in gearing as we know it today. It was in this period that the force pump, hydraulic pipe organs and the water clocks were invented. Perhaps the best known mathematician-engineer of the Hellenistic period is Archimedes who, among several contributions, gave us the science of "**hydrostatics**" and developed the **theory of mechanical advantage.**

1.4 ROMAN ENGINEERS

It is believed that the Romans contributed nothing to pure science but were very dynamic in the applied sciences. Their engineers could be described as civil engineers because their greatest activities were the building of roads, bridges, public buildings, aqueducts and sewers. The Roman engineers helped the advancement and improvement of everyday machinery.

The Roman engineers or architects made significant advances in the building of houses. It is believed that they re-invented the technique of central indirect heating, the original invention being attributed to the kingdom of Anatolia somewhere around 1200 B.C.

The modern concrete used in building houses and bridges was the invention of the Roman builders who first discovered cement. It can be said that the greatest contribution of early Roman engineers is in the field of building construction. They developed techniques for constructing huge buildings in a short period of time which was much less expensive than those of the antecedent centuries.

Roman engineers, though primarily civil engineers, nevertheless made some advances in already existing mechanical devices. For example, it was during the Roman times that a better press appeared and the use of the water wheel became extensive. Many wheel-shaped devices were developed for hoisting water and power machinery was improved. Water-mills were used to supply flour to the city of Rome. Other significant contributions of the late Roman Imperial Period included the invention of **trusses** and the **pendentive**.

1.5 THE ORIENTAL ENGINEERS

Most of the activities of the oriental engineers seemed to be confined to building of temples, an influence due to the propensity towards religious activities of the people. The contribution of the Indian engineers is primarily in their skills with iron works. The Arabic engineers, on the other hand, continued the activities of the Mesopotamian, Egyptian and Greek engineers. They made water clocks and tinkered with water wheels. In fact, it is believed the idea of perpetual motion was introduced by the Arabic engineers as a result of tinkering with water clocks and water wheels. These activities may have led to some of their contributions. They developed water power and made the first real practical use of the wind mill.

Another contribution by the oriental engineers was by the Chinese engineers. Their buildings were similar to the ones previously discussed, but in addition they had curved roofs. Their bridges also had distinct features. They built hanging bridges which were suspended by cables made from bamboo. Their engineers built canals for irrigation purposes. It is also believed that the wheelbarrow was invented by a Chinese engineer. Their engineers, like many ancient engineers, improved upon existing inventions. For example, they improved the clock by using the escapement, a mechanism that made it possible to control the speed of a clock and allow it to be driven by small power source.

1.6 THE EUROPEAN ENGINEERS

It appears that the early European engineers did not produce many original inventions rather they advanced existing ones. Their early engineers were mostly craftsmen who worked by rule of thumb after learning their trades through a system of apprenticeship. However, during the Middle Ages, a few scholars became interested in the physical sciences advancing the science of statics, the analysis of the forces in load bearing solid structures. There were some notable inventions around this period such as the flying machine. There was an increasing use of water power and during this period such devices as the water-powered hammer, and draw plates for drawing wire were all introduced.

Several advances were made in the High Middle Ages. These included advances in the structural forms and trusses used in building houses. Of course, the most significant type of houses were churches, specifically cathedrals, and castles. Medieval Europe made some advances in power machinery such as the water powered sawmills; however, the most significant contribution seems to have been the windmill. Other significant advances were the improvement of wheeled traffic. In fact, the first omnibus capable of carrying up to sixty passengers appeared around the 18th century. The European engineers advanced hydraulics engineering in the area of canal building more than their predecessors including the Roman engineers. Other engineering activities included ship building. Significant progress was made in engineering during the Renaissance. Engineering schools started to appear as well as defined engineering disciplines.

1.7 SECRETS OF THE SUCCESS OF ANCIENT ENGINEERS

It has been suggested that the secrets of the ancient engineering success were three-fold. First, they made use of such simple instruments and devices as they had. Second, they had unlimited manpower and had the ability to organize it. Third, they had infinite patience. If these facts are accepted to be true, then one needs to learn from the ancients. As one preparing for the engineering profession, it becomes important for students to exercise the last quality of the ancient engineers, namely: patience. You must spend time learning any subject matter, although sometimes such concepts may be difficult to master. Spend the time needed and have the patience to master the concept. It is advisable that engineering students not be hasty in completing learning tasks. Such haste will lead to errors and defects in the learning process.

SOURCES USED

Hodge, H., **Technology In The Ancient World**, Barnes & Noble Inc., 1992.

De Camp L.S., **The Ancient Engineers**, Dorset Press, New York, 1990.

PROBLEMS

1.1 Write a short essay on what you consider to be the driving force behind engineering activities both in the ancient time and in this modern time.

1.2 A belief in life-after death motivated the building activities in Egypt, What other reasons led to engineering activities in the ancient world? Write in about 200 -300 words how this same type of belief has influenced engineering activities today.

1.3 Describe how you think that the Egyptian builders moved heavy stones to the top of the pyramids. How is the same task achieved today? Is there any connecting principles between the approach used by ancient builders and construction workers of today?

1.4 Using resources in your library, write a short essay on how Archytas of Taras invented, the mechanical bird that flew by compressed air. Does this invention have any connection with the modern air-plane.

1.5 Write an essay on the theory of mechanical advantage.

1.6 Imagine how the catapult was used in warfare and describe why it was a powerful weapon. Compare and contrast the use of catapult and the heavy artillery used in the modern warfare.

1.7 List some similarities between the engineering activities of the ancient Roman engineers and the US Defense department.

1.8 The ancient engineers did not attend a formal engineering school. Describe how they received their training. What do you see as the main difference between them and you as a first year engineering student?

1.9 Write a short essay on the windmill, tracing its origin and its uses.

1.10 What are the significant contributions of (a) Roman engineers (b) Oriental engineers (c) Kushite engineers (d) Mesopotamia engineers and (e) Greek engineers?

1.12 Identify the reason Mesopotamia engineers pursued the construction of canals.

1.13 Elaborate on how the three main secrets of the success of ancient engineers can be applied by you as you go through your engineering education.

CHAPTER 2

ENGINEERING DISCIPLINES

2.1 INTRODUCTION

Engineers often do not receive the recognition due them. This is due in part to the fact that the populace is not truly knowledgeable as to what engineering is and what engineers do. Some students may have decided to be engineers because of the influence of parents or friends, not really knowing which engineering discipline to pursue. In this chapter, the various engineering disciplines are briefly explored. However, it must also be emphasized that the nature of engineering is changing and many are realizing that the boundaries between disciplines must be removed. A typical engineering team may consist of engineers from several different disciplines, and for the team to function effectively, each member of the team must have some minimum knowledge of what the other members of the team do. In spite of the trends to remove the barriers between disciplines, the various disciplines are going to maintain their distinct characteristics through the foreseeable future. Before discussing the various disciplines, the term "engineering" must first be defined. The agency that maintains engineering standards for the United States of America, known as the Accreditation Board for Engineering and Technology (ABET), defines engineering as follows:

> *Engineering is the profession in which a knowledge of the mathematical and natural sciences gained by study, experience, and practice is applied with judgment to develop ways to utilize, economically, the materials and forces of nature for the benefit of mankind.*

The above definition indicates that there is a common body of knowledge possessed by all engineers. In most engineering schools, the engineering students take the same courses for the first two years. It is only in the third year that the differentiation in disciplines begins. In the subsequent sections brief descriptions of each major engineering discipline is given.

2.2 AEROSPACE ENGINEERING

Aerospace engineering is the engineering discipline whose major interest is to study the flight of all kinds of vehicles operating under different speeds and altitudes. It encompasses all the phases of the research, design, and development of commercial or military aircraft, spacecraft, helicopters, missiles, and submerging ocean vehicles. The discipline consists of two major engineering subdivisions: aeronautical and astronautical. Aeronautical engineering is concerned with flights confined to earth's atmosphere while astronautical engineering is involved with space flights.

Several concerns must be addressed as an aircraft moves through the earth's atmosphere (e.g., the interaction between an aircraft and the air around it, the behavior of the structures, the stability and the control of the aircraft). Consequently, there are at least four areas of specialty within the discipline. They are aerodynamics, structural design, propulsion systems, and guidance and control.

Aerodynamic engineers are primarily concerned with what happens to the external surface of the aerospace vehicles. For example, as an aircraft moves through the air, forces are created which have either a positive effect (lift) or a negative effect (drag) on the aircraft. In addition, heat is generated as a result of the interaction between the air and the external surfaces of the aircraft operating at high speeds. The aerodynamics engineer must be capable of predicting the lift, the drag and heat generated, and design the external surfaces accordingly to handle these situations.

The aerospace engineer who specializes in structural design is concerned with the design of the aircraft structures so that they can withstand the high forces and extreme temperature ranges encountered during flight. As a result, the structural engineer must work closely with the aerodynamic engineer who must provide the information concerning these high forces and extreme temperatures. In addition, the structural engineer interacts with the aerodynamics engineer in developing the geometry of the wings and the fuselages. The structural engineer must design structures to withstand the effects of mechanical vibration and other dynamic forces resulting from flight of the vehicle.

The design of turboprops, turbo and fan jets, and the entire propulsion systems is the primary responsibility of the aerospace engineer who has expertise in the area of propulsion.

The development of the instruments that provide the information necessary to maneuver or control the aircraft is performed by the aerospace engineer with specialty in the area of guidance and control. These engineers, in addition, develop systems that guide and control the trajectories of missiles.

An aerospace engineering student must expect to study such subjects as heat transfer, fluid mechanics and structural design. In addition, the student will study the elements of propulsion and learn how to determine optimum wing and body shapes of an aircraft.

2.3 AGRICULTURAL ENGINEERING

Agricultural engineering is concerned with mass production of food. Therefore, it is the discipline that applies the knowledge of machines and the understanding of soil systems and the environment to create the techniques and the technology essential for continued production and processing of agricultural products. In order to carry out these two major functions, agricultural engineers specialize in at least four different areas. The first area is power machinery. The agricultural engineer who specializes in this area is concerned with the design and improvement of agricultural equipment such as tractors, harvesters and agricultural feed systems. The second area is food engineering. The food engineers are concerned with designing devices for handling and processing food products. In addition, they must minimize the use of energy and reduce waste and be concerned with the effect of waste on the environment. The third area of specialization is irrigation and soils mechanics. The agricultural engineer in this area deals with the design and improvement of methods of irrigation and irrigation systems, water drainage, control of erosion, and land management. The final area of specialization handles the design and development of structures for housing livestock and other farm products.

2.4 ARCHITECTURAL ENGINEERING

In the survey of the ancient engineers of Chapter 1, it becomes clear that the oldest engineering activities were primarily concerned with the building of temples, pyramids and houses. These were carried out by architects. The architects are primarily concerned with form and space and with the aesthetics of buildings. The work of architects requires the contribution from the architectural engineers with respect to design of components. Architectural engineers are mostly concerned with the structural integrity and safety of buildings as well as the aesthetics of the buildings. The architectural engineer additionally focuses in the analysis and design of materials used in building construction.

2.5 CIVIL ENGINEERING

Civil engineering is the name given to the oldest engineering activity. The term was first used in the 19th century to distinguish between the discipline that affects our everyday lives and that of military engineering whose major functions are to construct engines of war and the infrastructure necessary to support the military. The activities of this discipline are easily visible. For example, the water we drink, our roads and bridges, and dams are reminders of what civil engineers do. Some of the areas of specialization include structures, transportation, hydraulics and water resources, environmental, geotechnical and geodetics.

The structural engineer deals with the design of large buildings, bridges, dams, tunnels, towers and other large structures. Their designs generally take into consideration such natural phenomena as earthquakes or high winds that affect the stability of structures. This type of engineer may be found working in aerospace companies and construction firms.

The transportation engineer is responsible for planning, designing, constructing, and maintaining highways, airports, harbors and other facilities that are involved with the movement of people. In addition, they devise means of controlling traffic flow, such as with the traffic signals and signs. The flow of water through channels, conduits, canals, and dams are the primary concern of the hydraulics and water resources engineer. In addition, they design irrigation systems, flood control systems and drainage systems.

The environmental engineer is concerned with the safety of our environment. Consequently, the management of solid waste, air and water pollution is the central issue. They also design and maintain sewage treatment systems.

The analysis of the structural behavior of the soil and rocks on which we build is the responsibility of the geotechnical engineer. This engineer is concerned with the design of foundations and other support bases.

The geodetic engineer is responsible for the development of maps and provides topographical surveys that are useful to the transportation engineers.

Since the areas in which the civil engineers work are those that affect our every day lives, it is not surprising that most county and state engineers are civil engineers.

2.6 CHEMICAL ENGINEERING

Chemical engineering is concerned with the development of processes, and the design and the operation of plants in which materials undergo chemical changes during their manufacture. Chemical engineers, therefore, apply the laws of physical chemistry, physics and mathematics in the development of these processes. They utilize mathematical methods called optimization methods to arrange materials, facilities and energy to produce the most efficient and cost effective processes.

Chemical engineers work in pilot plants since they are responsible for mass production of materials that the chemists make in the laboratory, often in test tubes. A pilot plant determines the feasibility of carrying out a process to a larger scale than that developed in a laboratory. In a pilot plant, unit operations that are necessary to carry out the processes in large scale are developed. Unit operations are processes such as mixing, evaporation, filtration or other chemical processes that are combined by the chemical engineer to produce the desired commodity. The responsibilities of chemical engineers include the economic evaluation of new projects. Chemical engineers deal with issues such as material handling, storage and piping for the flow of fluid in process plants.

The chemical engineers are employed in the pharmaceutical industries, food processing plants, paper manufacturing plant, plastic industries and other plants where chemical processes are of concern. Their roles in pollution control are on the increase.

2.7 ELECTRICAL ENGINEERING

Electrical engineering deals with the application of electricity ranging from electric light, power systems to electronic appliances such as radios, radars and electronic computers. It is the largest branch of engineering. The areas of specialty in electrical engineering include power, electronics, communication, and computers.

The electrical power engineer is concerned with electric light and power. The production and distribution of electricity in both residential and industrial applications are his primary responsibilities. Therefore, he is involved in the design, manufacture, and use of generators, turbines, transformers, transmission lines, motors, and other heavy appliances that need electricity to operate.

The electronic engineer is concerned with the motion of electrons through metals. It is difficult today to live without coming into contact with devices that result from the work of electronic engineers. When one watches television or uses a calculator or computer, that person is enjoying the effort of electronic engineers. The many devices that we use that do not use high current are due to electronic engineers. They design circuits utilizing various electric elements such as integrated circuits, transistors, vacuum tubes or other similar types of devices that either produce or amplify electrical signals.

The electrical engineer with expertise in the area of communications is concerned with information transfer. Communication is either through the wire or wireless as in the use of satellites. The engineer who specializes in communications is responsible for the design of radios, telephones, televisions, digital information between computers, to name a few.

Computer engineers are responsible for the design, construction, and operation of computer systems. They interact with other electronic engineers to design the microprocessors found in the computer and many home appliances of today. It is important to note that they deal with not only the hardware problems of the computer but also the software issues.

2.8 INDUSTRIAL ENGINEERING

Industrial engineering is that engineering discipline that blends together the knowledge of mathematics, physical sciences, social sciences, and principles of engineering analysis, to design integrated systems that are capable of either delivering services or producing goods. Industrial engineers are primarily concerned with the design of manufacturing systems. In doing so, they deal with the effective methods of using money, materials, time, human, machinery, and energy.

Industrial engineers are always concerned with the improvement of the manufacturing systems and as a result, they are involved in production planning and control. To be effective they conduct studies commonly known as time and motion studies. The results of such studies allow them to optimize the handling of materials and the overall performance of the manufacturing system. They are concerned with such issues as quality control, minimizing waste of either materials or energy.

Some view the industrial engineer as the middle person between the management side of a business and the technical side. Their knowledge of both management issues and engineering issues contributes to their being often selected as top managers in the organization. Industrial engineers find employment in industrial manufacturing companies, hospitals, airline and many other settings where planning and cost containment are of concern.

2.9 MECHANICAL ENGINEERING

Mechanical engineering is, from our survey of ancient engineers, one of the oldest engineering disciplines. By far it is the broadest area of engineering, covering many areas dealing with energy and mechanical systems. As far as industry is concerned the mechanical engineer is ubiquitous. Mechanical engineering deals with machines, production of power, and manufacturing methods. It is that engineering discipline that is particularly concerned with forces and the motions they induce. There are many areas of specialty in mechanical engineering, however, these areas fall in one of two major categories: mechanical systems or thermal systems.

The area of mechanical systems encompasses the design of machines and mechanisms used for all kinds of manufacturing operations. In addition, engineers in this area are involved with the design of transportation modes such as automobiles, airplanes, ships, trains, . They are also involved in the design of various farming equipment such as tractors and lawn mowers. Within the mechanical system are engineers with strong backgrounds in vibrations and lubrication.

The engineer who specializes in thermal systems design works with other mechanical engineers in the development of power production systems such as boilers and turbines. These engineers are responsible for the design of pumping systems including the piping systems. They are concerned with controlled conditions. You appreciate their work during hot summers when you turn on your air conditioner or during cold winters when you turn on your heating system. Therefore, they are involved in the design of heating, ventilation, and air conditioning systems. Just in case you forget, you will not be able to leave meat or milk over night were it not for those engineers who design our refrigerating systems.

The mechanical engineer finds employment in any industrial setting, yes even in the electronics industry. You may ask what do they do there? Well, you know that the use of electric currents generate heat. The mechanical engineer must design the devices necessary to remove the heat generated in the electronic appliances. The point is that it is fruitless to name the types of companies that employ them since they are found in every type of industry where devices that move and utilize electricity are found.

2.10 NUCLEAR ENGINEERING

Nuclear engineering deals primarily with the use and management of energy derived from nuclear reactions. Nuclear engineers are involved with the development, design, and construction of power reactors. They are also involved in the fuel management of reactors. Since environmental concerns scare people when they hear of nuclear energy, nuclear engineers spend a considerable amount of time in safety analysis. This would involve risk assessment in case of nuclear reactor accidents and finding ways to prevent such accidents.

Nuclear engineers find employment with the Defense Department, specifically in the naval and nuclear weapons programs. They can also work for power companies which utilize nuclear energy for electricity generation. Because they must be involved in the actual design of reactors, architectural engineering firms who design housing units for this product hire them as well.

2.11 PETROLEUM ENGINEERING

Petroleum engineering deals with the extraction of liquid and gaseous hydrocarbon products from the earth (e.g. gasoline, heating and cooking gases). The activities of the petroleum engineer are essential for the survival of the modern industries and for the level of comfort enjoyed by all the industrialized nations of the world

Some of the areas of specialization include drilling and production. The drilling engineer is responsible for the design of drilling rigs and as such must understand rock formation. In addition, he must also have the knowledge of appropriate materials to be used in drilling operations. The production engineer's work begins once a well has been drilled. His function is that of directing the amount of raw products (oil crude or gas) to be extracted and to find ways to simulate production. In addition, he must design both storage and delivery systems for the fuel.

2.12 OTHER BRANCHES

There are other branches of engineering that have not been discussed. It does not mean that these engineering disciplines are not important. Due to space limitation only some of the better known disciplines have been described. Other important branches of engineering not included here are those that address biomedical, oceanographic, manufacturing, or environmental concerns. If you have already selected a particular engineering discipline or are not sure which discipline you would like to pursue, there are a few factors that you should consider before making a final decision. You should consider the availability of jobs by the time you graduate along with your area of interest. Equally important is your own ability. Some disciplines are more rigorous than others. Perhaps a major factor that should not be ignored is that of considering a discipline that will give you a broad base engineering education.

PROBLEMS

2.1 Define the term engineering and trace the origin of the word.

2.2 Give the reasons why you want to become an engineer.

2.3 Discuss what engineers should do in order to enhance their respect with the public.

2.4 What discipline of engineering are you considering? Give reasons why you are interested in this area.

2.5 Describe in detail the various areas of specialization in civil, electrical and mechanical engineering.

2.6 Identify the similarities between the areas of specialization in civil engineering and mechanical engineering.

2.7 Discuss the overlap between the activities of a chemical engineer and a mechanical engineer.

2.8 Interview a practicing engineer . Write a report on what you find out about the daily activities of this engineer.

2.9 What is the purpose of ABET?

2.10 Name the three branches of engineering that have the necessary background to design structures.

2.11 Why is mechanical engineering considered, by some, as the broadest area of engineering?

2.12 Discuss the problems faced by a nuclear engineer in today's environment conscious society.

2.13 What do you see as the reasons for the phasing out the Petroleum engineering curriculum by many engineering schools.

2.14 The mechanical and industrial engineers are both concerned with manufacturing. How can you differentiate the two types of engineers?

2.15 Compile a list of companies that would hire you when you graduate from engineering school. What skills do these companies expect of a graduate from engineering school.

CHAPTER 3

ENGINEERING AS A PROFESSION

3.1 INTRODUCTION

The engineering profession touches every aspect of our lives and, as such, it is a profession that demands utmost care, perseverance, and reliability. You may say well "so does every other profession," but the engineering profession is a little bit different in its service to mankind. It is true that in many societies engineers receive little recognition therefore, most do not understand the importance of this group of professionals. Consider the fact that even the medical profession today would not have attained its present level were it not for the technological advancement made by engineers in designing some of the equipment utilized in that profession. Furthermore, consider the fact that when a physician makes a mistake only a few people die. When engineers make mistakes in their designs the cost can be very exorbitant both in terms of human life and money. Many examples can be cited to dramatize this point but consider the two incidents that may stand out in most people's minds. The failure of the walkway of the Hyatt Regency Hotel in Kansas City, Missouri, led to the deaths of over a hundred people and injury to more than 180. What about the explosion of the Challenger in 1986? Seven lives were lost and several billions of dollars went up in smoke in a matter of seconds and years were spent in the redesign of the shuttle. Furthermore, the space program of NASA lost credibility with the public. These two incidents should convince you of the seriousness and the importance of this profession.

The use of the term "profession" has become so common that only a few actually reflect on the meaning of the term. Webster dictionary defines it as " *a calling requiring specialized knowledge and often long and intensive academic preparation.*" The engineering profession consists of individuals with a common basic knowledge of mathematics, physics, chemistry, and the ability to solve complex problems. In this chapter, we examine the elements of this profession including the basic training for the profession, and efforts involved in maintaining standards in the profession.

3.2 ENGINEERING CURRICULUM

The purpose of an engineering curriculum is to provide the student with the basic knowledge necessary to enter the engineering profession. In addition, it is designed to teach the student the basic methods required for successful problem solving. This includes procedures for analyzing a problem while evolving into a decision-making mode on how to go about solving the problem. Therefore, an engineering curriculum is developed around subjects that aid in teaching a student in conceiving and formulating solutions to stated problems as well as how to formulate problems.

An engineering curriculum is one that is well thought out with a fundamental need to establish specific criteria. The engineer utilizes materials and energy in creative activities. Therefore, an engineering curriculum includes courses that provide fundamental knowledge of energy and materials and their utilization. Since, engineers model nature, the basic knowledge must include mathematics, physics and chemistry or other physical sciences. In addition, because a good engineer is an integrator of knowledge, the engineering curriculum contains courses that teach this skill. These include social science courses and communication courses that provide skills in oral, written and graphical communications.

To insure that each engineering curriculum provides the students a basic knowledge to establish and sustain the student as he attempts to function as an engineer, the Accreditation Board for Engineering and Technology (ABET) maintains quality control over all engineering schools. The recognition of any engineering curriculum by ABET gives confidence to the public that students who have passed through the curriculum possess the minimum knowledge necessary to enter the engineering profession. While ABET does not specifically state the courses you must take, it has given five basic criteria. These criteria in effect, state that if an engineering curriculum is to be recognized by ABET, it must contain :
- One-half year of mathematics beyond trigonometry and algebra.
- One-half year of basic sciences.
- One year of engineering sciences.
- One-half year of engineering design.
- One-half year of humanities and social sciences.

In most engineering schools the first two years of study for all engineering disciplines contain the same courses. These courses cover mathematics, basic sciences and engineering sciences. Mathematical courses are calculus and differential equations. The basic sciences are physics and chemistry. The engineering sciences include courses in mechanics, thermodynamics, circuit theory and material science. During the last two years, generally speaking, the curriculum is discipline specific to give the student an in-depth knowledge in the chosen area of concentration. A sample of a mechanical engineering curriculum taken from the catalog of an ABET accredited mechanical engineering program is shown in Tables 3.1a and 3.1b. Note that this program allows the students to take two technical electives to broaden the students knowledge in engineering. Some schools now require that students take these courses in other engineering disciplines to give them an inter-discipline experience.

Table 3.1a. A typical Mechanical Engineering curriculum

FRESHMAN YEAR

FALL SEMESTER		SPRING SEMESTER	
Courses	Cr. HR	Courses	Cr. HR
ENG 101 FRESHMAN ENGLISH	3	ENG 102 FRESHMAN ENGLISH	3
MATH 163 CALCULUS I.....	4	MATH 164 CALCULUS II.....	4
CHEM 151 CHEMISTRY.......	3	PHY 221 PHYSICS I.......	3
CHEM 151L CHEMISTRY LAB..	1	PHY 221L PHYSICS II.....	1
ENGR 100L INTRO.TO ENGR.I	1	ENGR 101L INTRO.TO ENGR II	1
ENGR 113L ENGR. GRAPHICS	3	PE/AERO/BAND............	2
TOTAL	15	TOTAL	14

SUMMER SEMESTER

PHY 222 PHYSICS II.......	3
PHY 222L PHYSICS II LAB.	1
ENG 211 AMERICAN LITERATURE...3	
MATH 263 CALCULUS III....	3
TOTAL	10

SOPHOMORE YEAR

MATH 264 CALCULUS IV.....	3	MATH 303 ENGINEERING MATH	3
PHY 223 PHYSIC III......	3	ENGR 200 CIRCUIT I.......	3
ENGR 211 STATICS.........	4	ENGR 200L CIRCUIT I LAB..	1
ENGR 221 COMPUTER PROGRAM	3	ENGR 212 DYNAMICS........	4
HIST 201 AMERICAN HISTORY	3	ENGR 201 THERMODYNAMICS..	3
TOTAL	16	TOTAL	15

Table 3.1b. A typical Mechanical Engineering curriculum

JUNIOR YEAR			
Courses	Cr. HR	Courses	Cr. HR
ENGR 320 INTRO. TO DESIGN.	3	SPCH 230 BUSINESS AND PROFESSIONAL COMMUNICATION	3
ENGR 330 MATERIAL SCIENCE	3	ME 310 MATERIALS PROCESSING	3
ENGR 340 NUMERICAL ANALYSIS	3	ME 325 COMPUTER AIDED DESIGN	3
ME 321 MECHANISM DESIGN..	3	ME 322 DESIGN OF MACHINE ELEMENTS	3
CE 312 MECHANICS OF MATERIALS	3	CE 310 FLUID MECHANICS	3
CE 312L MECHANICS OF MAT. LAB	1	ME 352L MANUFACTURING PROCESS LABORATORY	1
ME 351L MEASUREMENTS LAB.	1		
TOTAL	17	TOTAL	16
SENIOR YEAR			
ENG 212 AMERICAN LITERATURE	3	HIST 202 AMERICAN HISTORY	3
ME 401L INSTRUMENTATION LAB.	1	ME 402L THERMAL FLUID SYSTEMS LABORATORY	3
ME 415 HEAT TRANSFER	3	ME 425 THERMAL FLUID SYSTEMS DESIGN	3
ME 450 CAPSTONE DESIGN PROJ.I	1	ME 451 CAPSTONE DESN.PROJ. II	1
ME 423 MACHINE DESIGN	3	ME 491 SENIOR SEMINAR	1
HUMANITY ELECTIVE	3	DESIGN ELECTIVE	3
TECHNICAL ELECTIVE	3	SOCIAL SCIENCE ELECTIVE	3
TOTAL	17	TOTAL	17

3.3 THE ESSENTIALS OF A SUCCESSFUL STUDENT

Engineering is a very rewarding but demanding profession and, as such, the preparation for a career in engineering in itself is very challenging. The engineering student must immediately recognize that he is entering a discipline that demands a lot of time and thought. In view of this it is necessary to consider oneself different from the rest of the student population both in pursuit of pleasures and in attitudes towards homework. Engineers are "doers"; they gain competence through experience. Therefore, success in engineering school may well depend on how much time one devotes to studying and to homework. Most freshmen often discover that high school study habits , in most cases, if applied in engineering school can result in failure. Poor study habits developed in high school must be changed to succeed in an engineering school. Because of the demands on   students, one may at times feel frustrated because he just "doesn't get it." Through counseling and observations, there are certain characteristics that an engineering student must posses to be successful. The characteristics listed here are not exhaustive but four essential ones have been selected. They are:

1. **Enthusiasm**. It is well known fact that people excel in those things about which they are enthusiastic. A successful engineering student must be eager to learn new concepts. In addition, the student must be self motivated. There may always be subjects that do not inspire interest and if one is not enthused and self-motivated, it will be difficult to learn these materials.

2. **Systematic**. A successful engineering student must learn to be systematic. He must develop the attitude of being orderly in what he does. There is always the need to rush and graduate and as such some students try to take courses without paying proper attention to the prerequisites required. Or there may be an effort to convince an academic advisor that one can do well in this or that course without the proper prerequisite. Just remember that the curriculum has been developed with the concept that knowledge is built on knowledge. So you may want to take a first course in mechanics, but you have not taken mechanics concepts as presented in physics. You are setting yourself up for failure or frustration while taking the course.

3. **Tenacity**. Engineers never give up. The solution of a problem may not be apparent at the start but the engineer must have the attitude that "if there is a problem, then there must be a solution." Therefore, they "hang in there" until they find the solution. This attitude is what we mean by tenacity. A successful student must be very patient. So you do not understand the topic covered in class. Go home and study the concept again. You still did not understand it from your text book; go to the library and find another book that has presented the material differently from your text book. You still do not understand then go to your professor. Most professors are willing to help but you must show them that you have made serious effort to understand the material. Notice, the order suggested. Most students want to run to their professor without

using library resources. You do yourself a good service by learning how to use your resources. After all that is what engineers do best: use available resources.

4. **Self discipline**. This word is becoming a "bad word" in the minds of many individuals in the society. There is an old Roman saying which translates from the Latin *"He is a winner who conquers himself."* This is probably the most important characteristic that you must possess as a student. There are many things on the campus that you would prefer doing over studying. There are many things that can give you pleasure, but pursuing them may cut into your study time. It may be necessary to ignore these activities. Such a decision is not easy unless you have total control by knowing your priorities. Self-discipline means that if the party of the year is going to take place tomorrow, but you have an examination the day after, what would you do: go for the party or study for your exam? An undisciplined person will definitely opt for the party instead of studying. It is easier to go for pleasure than for work. Self-discipline will also manifest itself in time management. One should plan adequate time for study. A good rule of thumb is that for every one hour you spend in class, you must at least spend three hours studying the materials presented in class in that particular course. For example, if you take a course that meets three hours a week, to be a "C" student you must at least study nine hours a week. If you are going to learn and master the subject you should first go over the theory of the particular topic and after you have mastered the concepts or the theory then you should solve many problems to help solidify the concepts. This means that you must do a lot of home work, more home work than was assigned in the class. A sample time management for a freshman student who is following the curriculum shown in Table 3.1 is shown in Table 3.2. It is our belief that a student who faithfully follows and has the aptitude for engineering *will definitely succeed*.

Table 3.2 A sample time management schedule for a first
semester student following Table 3.1

TIME	MON	TUE.	WED.	THURS.	FRI.	SAT.	SUN
6-7:30	P R E	P A R A	T I	O N &	BREAK	F A	S T
8-8:50	ENGR 113L^c	ENG 101^c	ENGR 113L^c	ENG 101^c	ENGR 113L^c	MATH 163S	PERSON AL
9-9:50	x	ENGR 113L^s	x	MATH 163^s	x	x	x
10-10:50	x	x	x	x	x	x	x
11 - 11:50	MATH 163^c	x	MATH 163^c	MATH 163^c	MATH 163^c	ENGR 100L^s	x
12 - 12:50P	LUNCH	LUNCH	LUNCH	ENGR 100L^c	LUNCH	LUNCH	LUNCH
1-1:50 (1:30)	CHEM 151L^s	CHEM 151^s	MATH 163^s	x	MATH 163^s	ENGR 100L^s	ENGR 113L^s
2-2:50	CHEM 151L^c	CHEM 151^c	x	CHEM 151^c	x	CHEM 151^s	x
3-3:50	x	MATH 163^s	x	CHEM 151^s	x	x	x
4-4:50	x	x	x	x	x	x	x
5-5:50	BREAK	BREAK	BREAK	BREAK	BREAK	x	x
6- 7	DINNER	DINNER	DINNER	DINNER	DINNER	DINNER	DINNER
7:30- 10	ENGR 100L^s	ENG 101^s	CHEM 151^s	ENGR 113L^s	ENGR 100L^s	PERSON AL	ENG 101^s
10:15 - 12:15	CHEM 151^s	ENG 101^s	ENGR 100L^s	MATH 163^s	ENG 101^s	x	ENGR 100L^s
12:30-		S	L	E	E	P	

Note: superscript c = in class; s = study time; x = same as entry
above it.

3.4 PROFESSIONAL REGISTRATION

Because engineers provide service to the society, it becomes
important to certify those who are able to function as engineers.
This certification, known as registration, began in the state of
Wyoming in 1907. The purpose of registration is to protect the
public from unqualified individuals who claim to be engineers.
When you are sick, you want to be attended by a competent and
licensed physician. Similarly, when you drive your car across a
bridge, you want to be sure that the bridge was designed by
competent engineers and maintained at the appropriate level. It
is clear that in most states no one can use the designation
"engineer" unless he or she is duly registered. In fact, some
states require that design classes be taught only by professors
who are registered engineers.

Registration involves four stages:

1. Obtain four years of engineering education. Graduation from an ABET accredited engineering program qualifies you for the second stage.
2. Pass the Fundamentals of Engineering Examination. This eight hour examination, covers fundamentals in mathematics, chemistry, physics, engineering mechanics, electrical science, thermodynamics, fluid mechanics, and economics. You stand a better chance of passing this examination if you take it in your senior year.
3. Obtain a minimum of four years post graduation engineering experience.
4. Pass the Principles and Practice of Engineering examination. This also is an eight hour examination tests the knowledge of principles involved in engineering practice in the area of your specialty. For example, if you are a mechanical engineer your examination will test principles and practice of mechanical engineering.

You may wonder what happens if you pass these examinations in one state and are licensed in that state and then you want to transfer to another state, can you transfer the results to the new state? Each state board of registration has its own rules and regulations, but in general, each accepts the examination results from another state.

3.5 RESPONSIBILITIES OF THE PROFESSIONAL ENGINEER

Engineering is a profession that interfaces the advances in science and technology with the needs of the society. Therefore, a professional engineer is an individual who by training and experience is able to utilize the advances in science and technology to create solutions that meet the needs of the society. A professional engineer is a highly motivated individual who has a strong desire to serve mankind by creating devices that make life comfortable.

Because a professional engineer is responsible for establishing the design criteria and processes, one of his major responsibilities is to stay current with scientific and technological discoveries. This means that a professional engineer must continuously educate himself by attending short courses, professional meetings and reading technical journals. It is his responsibility to support the activities of the profession by sharing his knowledge with other members of the profession. Furthermore, a professional engineer must be very careful in reporting results so as not to mislead the public since engineering decisions are based on reported data and facts. It is his responsibility to adhere to the codes and ethics defined by the profession. The reputation of the profession rides on the back of the professional engineers This means that one must be extremely careful in the practice of engineering. It is not acceptable for a professional engineer to be sloppy in design. To impress upon you the responsibility of engineers this section ends with a quotation from the Memoirs of Herbert Hoover, an engineer and the thirty-first president of the United States:

The great liability of the engineer . . . is that his works are out in the open where all can see them. His acts step by step, are in hard substance. He cannot bury his mistakes in the grave like the doctors. He cannot argue them into thin air or blame the judge like the lawyers. He cannot, like the architect, cover his failures with trees and vines, He cannot, like the politicians, screen his short -comings by blaming his opponents and hope that people will forget . The Engineer simply cannot deny that he did it. If his work does not work he is damned. . . .unlike the doctor, his is not a life among the weak. Unlike the soldier, destruction is not his purpose. Unlike the lawyer, quarrels are not his daily bread. To the engineer falls the job of clothing the bare bones of science with life, comfort, and hope.

3.6 PROFESSIONAL ORGANIZATIONS

Engineering, a profession with many disciplines, has many professional organizations and societies. For example, ASME (American Society of Mechanical Engineers), ASCE(American Society of Civil Engineers), IEEE (Institute of Electrical and Electronics Engineers, Inc.), to name a few. The purpose of these professional societies is to expedite the sharing of ideas among its members. They do this by publishing technical journals and magazines that contain important developments in the discipline, and by organizing conferences for exchange of ideas, short courses in current technologies or other needed areas of knowledge. Most of these organizations actively promote the profession and serve as a body that lobbies congress on issues related to engineering. They are highly involved in quality control in engineering education by their participation in ABET meetings and hearings.

As an engineering student you should make an effort to explore the organization of your chosen discipline. It is advisable to join the student section of this organization where you will begin to learn the services provided by the organization. Furthermore, your participation in the organization may provide you the opportunity to develop leadership skills. Even after graduation, you should be an active member by attending sectional or local meetings of the organization and paying your annual dues. In return you will meet other engineers, share ideas and make business contacts. These are just a few of the benefits of being an active member of your technical society.

3.7 ENGINEERING ETHICS

Quite often people say that a person is not acting professionally. What this generally means is that this individual has not conformed to the ethical standards of the profession. This brings up the question: what is ethics? Webster dictionary defines it as follows:

> *The discipline dealing with what is good and bad and with moral duty and obligation: principle of conduct governing an individual or group.*

Ethics is a very interesting subject in that many talk about it, but very few actually adhere to it. It is very difficult to talk of ethics without regards to religion. Because the question in the final analysis is: who determines what is right or wrong? It is accepted that Western-Civilization is rooted in "Judeo-Christian ethics." It is not our intention to follow the standard approach to discussing ethics. Rather, it is to remind you that to be ethical at all times means doing what is right in all circumstances and being truthful in every situation. People, especially politicians, like to do things that they know are wrong but because they are not written in their books of ethics, they do them and claim that they are not unethical.

People often claim that ethical decisions are difficult and often unequivocal. Perhaps the truth should be told and that is that people are afraid of the consequences that they will suffer because of being truthful. Many people ask for the truth when in reality they do not want it. When you tell the truth you run some risk either of losing a friend or of losing your job. Take for an example, an engineer is told by his/her supervisor to falsify a design data. It is not a hard decision to say no, except that the engineer fears losing employment. Of course, there should be no question as to whether such an order is correct or incorrect. The point is that being ethical is not difficult if one is willing to accept the consequences of being truthful. You should be reminded that truth will always prevail, it may not be today but one will eventually find comfort in being truthful. Additionally, do not ignore the fact that many unethical behaviors have been uncovered to the shame of those involved.

Because ethics requires the definition of an accepted standard, ABET has put forth what is termed the code of ethics for engineers. These are given in Table 3.3. If you examine the seven fundamental canons, you will notice that there are two main thrusts which are: truth and integrity. If you recall that our emphasis has been to tell the truth or to be truthful at all times, then you should have no problem in this area. To illustrate our point, canon 2 means that you have to be truthful. If you are a mechanical engineer why should you pose as a chemical engineer? If you are truthful to yourself, there should be at no time that one would act in a capacity in which one has no expertise.

Table 3.3 Code of Ethics of Engineers (source ABET)

FUNDAMENTAL PRINCIPLES

Engineers uphold and advance the integrity, honor and dignity of the engineering profession by

I.   using their knowledge and skill for the enhancement of human welfare;

II. being honest and impartial, serving with fidelity the public, their employers and clients;

III. striving to increase the competence and prestige of the engineering profession and;

IV. supporting the profession and technical societies of their discipline.

THE FUNDAMENTAL CANONS

1. Engineers shall hold paramount the safety, health and welfare of the public in the performance of their professional duties.

2. Engineers shall perform services only in the areas of their competence.

3. Engineers shall issue public statements only in an objective and truthful manner.

4. Engineers shall act in professional matters for each employer or client as faithful agents or trustees, and shall avoid conflict of interest.

5. Engineers shall build their professional reputation on the merit of their services and shall not compete unfairly with others.

6. Engineers shall act in such a manner as to uphold and enhance the honor, integrity and dignity of the profession.

7. Engineers shall continue their professional development throughout their careers and shall provide opportunities for professional development of those engineers under their supervision.

SOURCES USED

Burghardt, M.D., **Introduction To Engineering**, Harper Collins Publishers Inc., New York, 1992.

Eide, A.R., R. Jenison, L. Mashaw and L. Northup, **Engineering Fundamentals and Problem Solving,** Second edition, McGraw-Hill Book Co., New York, 1986.

Holmes, A.F., Ethics- **Approaching Moral Decisions**, Inter-Varsity Press, Downers Grove, Illinois, 1986.

Memoirs of Herber Hoover, Vol. 1, Years of Adventure, Macmillan Publishing Company, 1951.

Wright P.H., **Introduction To Engineering**, second edition, John Wiley & Sons, Inc., New York, 1994.

PROBLEMS

3.1   Discuss in detail why the engineering profession is different from all others.

3.2   Evaluate the curriculum of your chosen area of engineering with regard to ABET criteria.

3.3   Write out a plan of study that could lead to your graduating from your engineering school in the least possible time.

3.4   Develop a weekly schedule for this semester so that you have at least 3 hours of study time per week for every one hour in class.

3.5   Summarize the characteristics of a successful engineering student. Describe how you can apply them.

3.6   Explain why it is important to follow the sequence of courses listed in your curriculum.

3.7   Why is it important to become a registered professional engineer?

3.8   Describe what you think ought to be done by the engineering profession to insure that all who practice engineering should be duly registered.

3.9   Write out your plan for becoming a registered engineer.

3.10 Interview the president of the student chapter of the professional organization for your chosen discipline. In your report indicate what is the need for the organization, the process of becoming a member and the benefits to you.

3.11 Modify the engineering ethics so it applies to an engineering student.

3.12 Summarize an interview with an engineering professor that focuses on how he/she applies the engineering ethics to engineering education.

NOTES

CHAPTER 4

ENGINEERING PROBLEM SOLVING METHODOLOGY

4.1 INTRODUCTION

Engineers are best known for solving various forms of problems that face the society in the areas of human comfort and enjoyment. The thing that sets engineers apart is the manner in which they approach problems . The author had this confirmed by a salesman in Orlando, Florida. A salesman approached the author with a proposition to buy into a vacation type resort plan. After making a presentation that lasted nearly an hour, the salesman allowed me to ask questions. At the onset of questioning, the salesman asked "are you by any chance an engineer?" To which he received the response, "Why?" He then said that several individuals have raised questions similar to the ones the author has raised and all these persons were engineers. The author laughed and said "Yes, I am an engineer." The point of this is that engineers are trained to follow certain procedures in solving problems. As an engineering student you will learn to think in a certain way. You will learn how to speak the engineer's language and reason like an engineer. As we will show shortly, once you learn the discipline of analyzing and solving problems in a certain format, you will amaze yourself as to how easy it will become to tackle difficult problems in an organized manner. The whole purpose of solving problem in a certain manner is that it helps to organize one's thinking. Since an organized thought means a plan, it follows that it will be ease to formulate plans for solving problems.

The purpose of this chapter is, therefore, to help you formulate a plan for solving various problems that you will encounter as an engineering student and later as an engineer. Once the methodology for solving problems has been presented, it is important to discipline yourself to follow the given approach. With constant practice you will train your mind to think in a certain logical manner .

4.2 PROBLEM FORMULATION

One of the most frustrating thing to do as a student is to go into an exam and do your best in solving a problem only to discover that you have solved the wrong problem or that what you thought was the problem was in fact a misunderstanding on your part. This happens too often even among some practicing engineers. It is for this reason that it may well be said that most of the engineering design activity is spent defining the problem. If little time is spent in this activity, one may create serious problems in the solution phase.

It should be emphasized that before you commence to solve any problem, you must clearly understand the problem. It is essential that you spend some time to clarify the problem especially if the problem is stated in a nebulous fashion. In formulating the solution you must include as much information as possible that relates to the problem. More will be said about problem formulation and definition in Chapter 5.

4.3 SOLUTION FORMAT

It has been previously stated that engineers like to solve problems using identical approaches that involves special methods of organization . This approach is often referred to as **the scientific problem-solving method**. Adhering to this method allows you to develop a certain type of mental attitude for solving any problem. Another advantage of this method is that it allows you to be organized in your thinking as you solve the problem. If one carefully applies this approach, an aptitude will be developed that will permit satisfactory solution of most engineering problems. This method generally involves six steps, with minor variations occurring in the first step.

Step 1: Problem statement

Describe the problem to be solved. The description must contain all the essential information regarding the problem. To document your solution properly, you must ask two important questions: what essential information is given and what is to be determined? The answers to both questions may consist of short statements or a set of defined symbols.

Step 2: Diagram

It is essential at this point to visualize the problem by preparing a sketch or a diagram of the process taking place. The diagram should show the physical set up of the problem and must contain all relevant dimensions.

Step 3: Theory

In order to obtain a solution, you must describe a relationship between what is given and what is to be found. Most people describe this process as **modeling**. It consists of simply developing a mathematical equation to describe the relationship between an input and an output. Sometimes, it may mean stating a fundamental law involved in a problem. For example, if you wish to solve a problem that involves motion, Newton's second Law may be stated as one of the theories for the solution of the problem.

Step 4: Assumptions

This step may in some problems precede step 3. You must state clearly the assumptions you have made to simplify the problem solution since different assumptions may lead to different results. This step must be carefully executed because if you do not make the appropriate assumptions your solution may not be acceptable, or if you make a wrong assumption you may not be able to simplify the problem.

Step 5: Solution

Present the solution in steps easy to follow by another person. The purpose, of course, is to give someone the ability to check your solution. Some instructors do not actually grade your final answer as they are more interested in how you actually arrived at the solution. You may obtain a correct numerical answer of a problem by making series of what can be termed self-compensating errors. Therefore, the steps are in fact a more reliable judge as to the correctness of the solution than the actual result. What we have said applies even for the practicing engineer, whose solution may be checked by another engineer. In summary, **document your solution by including all steps. Be comprehensive.**

Step 6: Verification and Final Results

At the end of the solution, you need to verify the result, if this is possible. You must check the solution accuracy, making sure that no errors are present. Always ask "**Is this solution reasonable**?" If you are satisfied that your solution is correct, then identify the final answer by either underscoring it with double lines or by putting a box around it.

An example that illustrates these steps is given in Figure 4.1. This figure is a representation of a sheet of what is known as an engineering pad for which the finer grids have been omitted. Note that the top row contains five columns. The first is blank. The second is used to indicate the due date. The third is for course and problem identifications. The fourth is for your name beginning with your last name. The last consists of the portion used for pagination.

4.4 DIMENSIONS

Engineering deals with physical quantities such as length, time, mass, and temperature. These physical quantities are referred to as dimensions. These quantities can be grouped into two categories: **primary** and **secondary**. Primary quantities, also known as **basic dimensions**, are small groups of dimensions from which all others can be derived. In primary quantities we set up arbitrary scales of measures.   The secondary quantities are those whose dimensions are derived or expressible in terms of the primary dimensions. For example, suppose we choose as primary quantities length(L), time(T), and mass(M). Secondary quantities such as velocity and density may be expressed in terms of the basic dimensions. The dimension of velocity(V) is derived in terms of length and time as $V = L/T$. Similarly, the dimension of density (ρ) is given by $\rho = M/L^3$.

Dimension is an important guide as to the nature of an equation that is based on physical quantities. If an equation is written that relates physical quantities then the dimensions of the left side of the equation must be the same as the right side.

If this condition is true, the equation is said be **dimensionally homogeneous.**

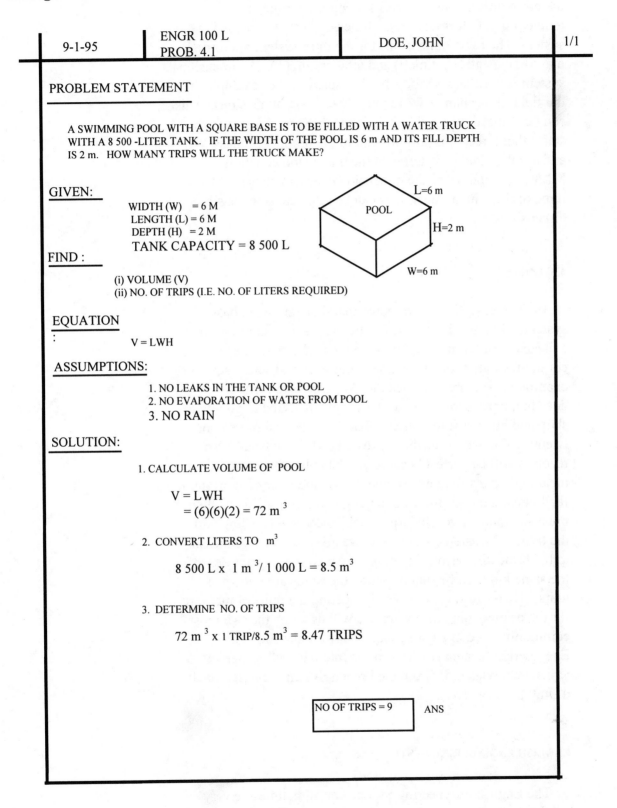

| 9-1-95 | ENGR 100 L PROB. 4.1 | DOE, JOHN | 1/1 |

PROBLEM STATEMENT

A SWIMMING POOL WITH A SQUARE BASE IS TO BE FILLED WITH A WATER TRUCK WITH A 8 500 -LITER TANK. IF THE WIDTH OF THE POOL IS 6 m AND ITS FILL DEPTH IS 2 m. HOW MANY TRIPS WILL THE TRUCK MAKE?

GIVEN:

WIDTH (W)   = 6 M
LENGTH (L) = 6 M
DEPTH (H) = 2 M
TANK CAPACITY = 8 500 L

L=6 m
POOL
H=2 m
W=6 m

FIND :

(i) VOLUME (V)
(ii) NO. OF TRIPS (I.E. NO. OF LITERS REQUIRED)

EQUATION:

$V = LWH$

ASSUMPTIONS:

1. NO LEAKS IN THE TANK OR POOL
2. NO EVAPORATION OF WATER FROM POOL
3. NO RAIN

SOLUTION:

1. CALCULATE VOLUME OF POOL

$V = LWH$
$= (6)(6)(2) = 72 \text{ m}^3$

2. CONVERT LITERS TO m^3

$8\,500 \text{ L} \times 1 \text{ m}^3 / 1\,000 \text{ L} = 8.5 \text{ m}^3$

3. DETERMINE NO. OF TRIPS

$72 \text{ m}^3 \times 1 \text{ TRIP}/8.5 \text{ m}^3 = 8.47 \text{ TRIPS}$

NO OF TRIPS = 9   ANS

Figure 4.1 A sample solution format

There are three basic systems of dimensions. The first system considers mass(M), length(L), time(t) and temperature(T) as the basic dimensions. Force(F), Length(L), time(t) and temperature(T) form the basic dimensions for the second system. The basic dimensions for the third system are force(F), mass(M), length(L), time(t) and temperature(T). A dimensional system is used to describe a field of science. For example, in the field of mechanics we require three basic dimensions. This can be realized by considering Newton's Second Law which states that force(F) is proportional to the product of mass(M) and acceleration, or in terms of the dimension equation, $F = ML/t^2$. Depending on the dimensional system chosen, only three of the primary quantities can be selected as the basic dimensions.

4.5 UNITS

In the last section it was noted that there are three basic systems of dimensions. The implication is that unless we have a means of differentiating between them, there will be communication problems among engineers and scientists. For example, if you are informed that Mr. Doe is ten lengths tall, does that make sense to you? Or if you are asked to go into a shop and buy a gift for a friend that does not cost more than twenty. You will immediately respond "twenty what?" Your reaction will be correct because you have been given a meaningless instruction. To avoid this kind of confusion and to facilitate communication among engineers and scientists there must be common vocabularies established when dealing with the basic dimensions. Therefore, we give quantitative measures to the basic dimensions in terms of which other quantities of the same kind can be stated. These measures are known as units. There are several ways of selecting the units of measure for the primary dimensions but we will describe the two most commonly used in engineering. They are the English Engineering System (EES) and the International System of Units, abbreviated SI (from the French Systeme International d'Units).

ENGLISH ENGINEERING SYSTEM (EES)

The English Engineering System can sometimes be very confusing when used in mechanics problems. This is due in part to the fact that mass and force are selected as basic dimensions. The unit of force is the pound force (lbf), the unit of mass is pound mass (lbm), the unit of length is foot, unit of time is seconds, and the unit of temperature is Rankine (^{o}R).

The confusion in using this system can be seen by considering Newton's:

$$F = ma \qquad (4.1)$$

If we apply the units defined above to equation (4.1), it will not be dimensionally homogenous. Therefore, it is written as

$$F = \frac{ma}{g_c} \qquad (4.2)$$

where g_c is a constant of proportionality necessary to make the equation dimensionally homogeneous. To determine the units of g_c a basic definition is utilized. A force of one pound (1 lbf) is the force that gives a pound mass (1 lbm) an acceleration equal to the standard acceleration of gravity of 32.17 ft/sec^2 on earth. From (4.2):

$$1 \text{ lbf} = (1 \text{ lbm} \times 32.2 \text{ ft/sec}^2)/g_c$$

giving

$$g_c = 32.17 \text{ lbm/lbf.sec}^2$$

SI UNITS

The SI units are more widely used internationally than the EES. This system of units is yet to make great strides in the United States, although its use is increasing. There are three classes of the units: **base units, supplementary units** and **derived units**. The base units consist of seven physically defined units. The units and the accepted symbols are given in Table 4.1. The supplementary units are two geometrically defined units (see Table 4.2). This class was introduced because there was no consensus as to whether these quantities belong to the base or derived units. A **radian** is the plane angle with its vertex at the center of a circle and subtended by an arc whose length is equal to the radius. A **steradian** is the solid angle with its vertex at the center of a sphere and enclosing an area of the spherical surface equal to that of square with sides equal in length to the radius. The derived units are those obtained by combining the base units, supplementary units, or other derived units. Those with special names and

Table 4. 1 Base units

Quantity	Unit	Symbol
Length	meter	m
mass	kilogram	kg
Time	second	s
Temperature	kelvin	K
Current	ampere	A
Luminous intensity	candela	cd
Amount of substance	mole	mol

Table 4. 2 Supplementary units

Quantity	Unit	Symbol
Plane angle	radian	rad
Solid angle	steradian	sr

symbols are listed in Table 4.3.

There are at least two factors that make the SI units attractive. The unit can be scaled (magnified or reduced) by using multiplying prefixes. The commonly accepted prefixes and their symbols are shown in Table 4.4. The other attractive feature is that the unit is coherent. This means that there is a one to one relationship between a derived unit and base units. For example, the unit of force is newton ($kg \cdot m/s^2$) because it is the force required to give a mass of 1 kg an acceleration of $1 \ m/s^2$. The unit of work is the Joule ($N \cdot m$), which is the result of a force of one newton operating through a length of one meter. Note that in each case the factor relating the derived and base units is one. This coherence characteristic helps to avoid the confusion between mass and force as in the English Engineering system. The unit of mass is clearly different from the unit of force.

Table 4. 3 Common derived units

Quantity	Name	Symbol	Base units
Force	Newton	N	$kg \cdot m \cdot s^{-2}$
Pressure	Pascal	Pa	$kg \cdot m^{-1} \cdot s^{-2}$
Work	Joule	J	$kg \cdot m^2 \cdot s^{-2}$
Power	Watt	W	$kg \cdot m^2 \cdot s^{-3}$
Resistance	Ohm	Ω	$kg \cdot m^2 \cdot s^{-3} \cdot A^{-2}$
Conductance	Siemens	S	$kg^{-1} \cdot m^{-2} \cdot s^{-3} \cdot A^2$

Table 4. 4 Commonly used Prefixes

Number	Exponential Form	Prefix	Symbol
0.000 000 001	10^{-9}	nano	n
0.000 001	10^{-6}	micro	μ
0.001	10^{-3}	milli	m
1 000	10^{3}	kilo	k
1 000 000	10^{6}	mega	M
1 000 000 000	10^{9}	giga	G

RULES FOR UTILIZING SI UNITS

Because of the uniqueness of SI unit system in assigning a precise meaning to any given symbol, its use calls for special care. There are specific guidelines that must be followed and a few of these are given below.

1. Unit symbols are written in lowercase Roman letters except when the symbol is from a proper name such as Newton and in this case the first letter is capitalized. The use of a period after a symbol, except at the end of a sentence is not allowed.

2. A dot, or a space, should be used for the multiplication of units. For example, we can write N·m or N m but not Nm.

3. A prefix should be used to keep numerical values between 0.1 and 1000. For example 23 000 Pa could be written 23 kPa.

4. When using a prefix, no space should be used between the prefix and unit symbol (e.g. write GPa and not G Pa).

5. In writing long numbers, commas should not be used since in some countries the comma is used in place of a decimal point. Instead use spaces to write numbers. For example, you may write 5 450 000 and not 5,450,000. However, if the number is small (less than 1) then use a zero before the number (e.g. 0.0135 not .0135).

6. Avoid the ambiguous use of the slash mark. For example, you should write N/m^2 and not N/m/m.

7. When performing calculations, numbers should be represented in terms of their base or derived units by converting all the prefixes to powers of 10. At the end of a calculation, express the final result using a single prefix. For example,

$$30 \text{ kN x } 5 \text{ Mm} = [30(10)^3 \text{ N}][5(10)^6 \text{ m}]$$
$$= 150(10^9) \text{ N m} = 150 \text{ GN m}$$

4.6 UNITS CONVERSION

The SI unit is becoming the global unit, however, there is much engineering and scientific information that is still in other systems of units. Because of this it becomes essential for the engineer to be able to convert from one system to the other. This situation may be seen in drawings generated in Europe, for example, for a plant in the U.S.; the manufacturing engineers must convert the dimensions on the drawings to the English Engineering System unit in order to produce the parts. However, in doing this, it must be kept in mind that the physical quantity must never change. For example, a length of 1 foot is a physical quantity which must correspond to 304.80 mm. To convert from one system of unit to another requires **a systematic approach and great care**. An illustration is given in Example 4.1.

Example 4.1
Convert the standard acceleration, g, from English Engineering unit to SI unit. Assume $g = 32.2 \text{ ft/s}^2$.

Solution
The first step is to **ascertain the expected unit at the end of the conversion**. In this case, the expected unit is m/s^2. The second step is to find the conversion factor between a foot and a meter (see Appendix A), 1 ft. = 0.3048 m. The procedure is as follows:

$$g = 32.\ 2 \text{ ft x } 1/s^2$$

$$g = \frac{32.2 \, ft}{1} \text{ x } \frac{0.3048 \, m}{ft} \text{ x } \frac{1}{s^2} = 9.81 \text{ m/s}^2$$

The above example is relatively easy, however, conversion can be complicated when we deal with equations given in a particular system of unit. To illustrate how to deal with this problem consider the next example.

Example 4.2

An engineer whose job deals with applications in fluid flow over free surfaces wrote a simplified formula for calculating a dimensionless quantity called Froude number (the ratio of inertia force to gravitational force). Because the engineer works with the EES unit, the Froude number, Fr, is expressed as:

$$Fr = 0.1762 \, Vh^{-0.5}.$$

V is the velocity in ft/s and h is the height in feet. The engineer wants to have an equivalent equation applicable to the SI units.

Solution

The key to the conversion lies in the fact that every equation must be dimensionally homogeneous. The equation is

$$Fr = 0.1762 \, Vh^{-0.5} \qquad \text{(a)}$$

Note that the left side of the equation has no units associated with it. If equation (a) is to be dimensionally homogeneous, it follows that the units associated with the constant value (0.1762) must be such that the right side of (a) is also unitless. Let C = 0.1762, then

$$Fr = CVh^{-0.5} \qquad \text{(b)}$$

Squaring both sides of (b) and solving for C gives

$$C^2 = (Fr)^2(h)/V^2 = (Fr^2)(ft)/(ft^2/s^2) = Fr^2(s^2/ft)$$

It is clear that the unit of C^2 is s^2/ft. Therefore, the new C', constant must have units of s^2/m. Convert C^2 to s^2/m as follows:

$$C' = \frac{C^2}{1} \, x \, \frac{s^2}{ft} \, x \, \frac{ft}{0.3048 \, m} = 3.2808 \, C^2 s^2/m = 0.1019 \, s^2/m$$

The result is C' = 0.3190 hence the new equation is
$$Fr = 0.3190 \, Vh^{-0.5} \qquad \text{(c)}$$

4.7 ERRORS

The unit is the quantitative measure of dimension. The implication is that the physical quantities in dimension such as length or time must be determined by some measurements. For example, suppose that you work with a utility company mounting electric posts. There may be the need to know the length of each post so at least it can be known how much of it has to go into the ground for the purpose of stability. Immediately you realize that the post has to be measured. Suppose, the post has already been cut to a certain unknown length . It is very likely that you may not measure the post to its actual length and in that case you have introduced an error. Error, therefore, is the difference between the true value and the measured value of a quantity.

Errors may be caused by several factors. It could be due to the malfunction of a measuring instrument. Or it could result from the failure on the part of the user to record correctly the reading of the instrument. Regardless of the source of error in measuring physical quantities, it is generally of two kinds: **error of accuracy** and **error of precision**. Accuracy error is the error that persists when average readings of an instrument deviates from the true value. For example, suppose that a pressure gage is used to measure the pressure of air in a tire. Further more, suppose it is known that the tire pressure is 210 Pascals, but the average of 5 readings of the pressure gage is 205 Pascals. It can be concluded that the pressure gage is not accurate. On the other hand, precision error is that observed when successive measurements of a fixed quantity give different readings. For example, if the previous pressure gage gave readings of 200, 205, 209, 215 and 206 Pascals, it may be said that there is an error of precision with the gage. A question may be raised of how to estimate these kinds of errors? The accuracy error in an instrument can be estimated only through calibration of the instrument using a standard instrument. Sometimes, the vendor may supply a calibration curve to help estimate the error. The precision error is estimated by using a rule which says that the precision error is one half the least count of the instrument. For example, consider the instrument shown in Figure 4.2 (voltmeter). Notice that the least count is 1 Volt therefore, the expected precision error is to be within 0.5

Volt. Because of errors it is always advisable to carry out an error analysis in any experimental work. Some of the parameters that are involved in error analysis are discussed in Chapter 10.

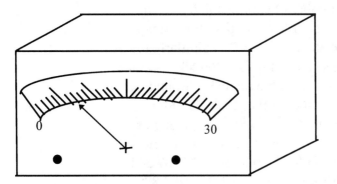

Figure 4.2 Voltmeter

4.8 SIGNIFICANT FIGURES AND ACCURACY

In reporting any data either as a result of experiment or calculations, there is always the question of how to record the numerical values involved and how many of the digits or figures are significant. A significant figure is any digit, including zero, provided that it is neither used to locate the position of the decimal point nor has the digit to the left of a zero. For example 0.003 has 1 significant figure where as 1.003 has four significant figures. Significant figures must be correctly used because the accuracy in a result is indicated by the number of the significant figures (digits) used. As a guide, three significant digits indicate that maximum error is 1 percent in the result, while four significant digits indicate 0.1 percent error, and so on.

It is sometimes confusing to say how many significant figures that are in a number when it ends with zeros. For example, how many significant figures are there in the number 5000? It could be any where from one to four significant figures. In order to clarify this situation it is best to write numbers using powers of 10. In doing so we can adopt one of two approaches: the scientific notation or engineering notation. In the scientific notation one digit is specified to the left of the decimal point and the rest appear to the right. For example,

5000 in scientific notation may be written as $5(10^3)$ if it is desired to indicate one significant figure or $5.000(10^3)$ for four significant figures. Engineering notation, on the other hand, expresses the exponent in multiples of three. For example, 5000 is written as $5(10^3)$ and 0.000322 is $322(10^{-6})$. In calculations that involve multiplication, division, addition, or subtraction, the final result should be the number of significant digits that are in the number with the least significant digits. For example the quotient $3.816/1.25 = 3.0528$ becomes 3.05. Similarly the product 3.816 x 2.4554, using a calculator, is 9.369 8064 so the product is 9.370. We have rounded off the number. Rounding off of numbers follows a simple rule. If the result should contain n significant figures, then if the n+1 digit is greater or equal to five then round the last significant figure up, otherwise round the figure down. For example, the numbers 3.0567 and 2.8214 rounded to three significant figures are 3.06 and 2.82.

PROBLEMS

4.1 How many significant figures are there in (a) 40 (b)0.005 (c) 5.000 (d) 0.00356 (e) 0.003560?

4.2 Express the following in scientific notation using 3 significant figures. (a) 900 (b) 9890 (c)9897 (d) 0.01893 (e) 12.1379 (f) 12.1679 (g) 0.00032 (h)0.00000012

4.3 Perform the following operations expressing the result in the appropriate significant figures.
(a) 181.34 + 1 930.4582 (b) 23.458 x 2.30078
(c) 134.20/2.00540

4.4 Convert the following to SI base units using the proper significant figures.
(a) 300 in (b)230 acres c)189.8 lbm
(d) 450.6 lbf (e) 523.52 ft^3/min (f) 44 ft/s
(g) 32.17 ft/s^2 (h) 14.7 lbf/in^2 (i) 100 ft-lbf
(j)125 hp (k) 1268.9 Btu/lbm (l) 205.45 gal/h

4.5 An object has a mass of 56 slugs. What is its mass in kilograms?

4.6 An astronaut weighs 165 lb. What is his mass (a) in slugs (b) in kilogram?

4.7 What is the weight of the astronaut of problem 4.6 in newtons on the moon, where the acceleration due to gravity is 5.30 ft/s^2

4.8 Determine whether or not the following equations are dimensionally homogeneous.

(a) $Q = kL\sqrt{2g}\ H^{1.5}$

where,

Q = discharge (m^3/s)
k = a pure number
L = length (m)
H = head (m)
g = acceleration due to gravity

(b) $V = \dfrac{1.5 m^{0.5} \sqrt[3]{S^2}}{\sqrt[6]{R}}$

where, v is velocity, S and R have units of length, and m is slope.

4.9 An architect erects a structure that is 2.5 m high. Its cross-section is a rhombus. It is to be fitted with a drum that touches all the four sides of the rhombus. The space between the drum and the inner wall of the structure is to be filled with concrete mix. If the cost of material and labor is $300/m³, what is the cost for filling the space with concrete? The angle between the left edge and the bottom edge of the rhombus is 75°.

4.10   The velocity of a moving fluid can be determined using the formula

$$V = 0.045\sqrt{\Delta P}$$

where,

   V = velocity, m/s

   ΔP = difference between total and static

   pressure, in Pascals

rewrite the equation for use in the English system of unit.

4.11   The flow rate through a channel can be determined using a weir by the following formula:

   $Q = 5.4LII^{1.5}$

where

   Q = discharge rate, ft³/s

   L = length of weir, ft

   H = height of fluid above crest, ft

For a weir length 1.5 m and fluid of height 2.2 m above crest, what is the flow rate in m³/s?

4.12   Two sprockets are to be connected by a chain for driving a conveyor system. The first sprocket is 128 mm in diameter and the second is 485 mm in diameter. If the center to center distance is 755 mm, what is the length of the chain?

4.13   A kerosene tank with a diameter of 1.5 m is placed so that it lies on its side on a horizontal surface. At an instant when the depth of kerosene in it is 250 mm from the horizontal, what is the weight of the kerosene left in the tank if the length of the tank is 2.7 m. Assume that the specific weight of the kerosene is 8.07 kN/m³.

SECTION TWO

ESSENCE OF ENGINEERING DESIGN

Obtaining Data for design purposes

INTRODUCTION TO SECTION TWO

Section Two contains the essentials that define engineering design activities. As an engineering student you will discover that most of the problems you solve in class have one right answer, unfortunately, in engineering design there may be several right solutions to a particular problem. This section is organized in a way to allow you to understand the connection between several seemingly disjointed courses you will take and to understand how they support the design process. You are first introduced to the design process. Because the design process involves a series of decisions, those activities that allow you to make meaningful design decisions are considered. To make a design decision, you need to analyze the problem. This may include analysis of mechanical, electrical, or energy systems. Hence, you are introduced to analysis of these types of systems in Chapters 6 through 8. Since analysis may be time consuming, in Chapter 9 you are introduced to the computer tools, that aid the engineer in the analysis stage. In the course of some analysis, you may have to conduct experiments to obtain certain data, therefore, in Chapter 10, you are introduced to methods of handling data. After analysis, it becomes necessary to select the best solution among several possible solutions. This requires that a criteria that may depend on costs be set, therefore, you are introduced to decision tools such as Optimization in Chapter 11 and Engineering Economy in Chapter 12 .

NOTES

CHAPTER 5

DESIGN PROCESS

5.1 INTRODUCTION

Engineering design is one of the most fascinating and challenging activities of the engineer. However, many engineers have their own definition of design. One thing that is clear is that the name engineer comes from an old Latin word **in generare** which means to create. If in the early history of engineering, engineers were viewed as individuals who create, then engineering design is a creative process which a solution is provided to a perceived need or problem. This view is adopted because when we think of design we associate it with a product. The product today may not simply be a device. For example, software is a product where the design process is applied. In order to examine the design process, a working definition for design is essential. Perhaps the best definition of engineering design is that given by ABET:

> *Engineering design is the process of devising a system,*
> *component, or process to meet desired needs. It is a*
> *decision-making (often iterative), in which the basic*
> *sciences and mathematics and engineering sciences are*
> *applied to convert resources optimally to meet a stated*
> *objective. Among the fundamental elements of the design*
> *process are the establishment of objectives and*
> *criteria, synthesis, analysis, construction, testing,*
> *and evaluation.*

The definition of engineering design, as stated above means that **the design process** may be viewed as the road map that guides the designer from the problem to its solution. Various models have been advanced for describing the design process. These models can be classified into two major categories: **descriptive** and **prescriptive**. The descriptive model views the design process as sequential activities that occur during a given design. The prescriptive model is a paradigm of activities that ought to be followed in the design process. The difference between the two models lies in the mind set that they try to develop in the designer. The descriptive model seeks to focus the designer on the solution of the problem. However, the prescriptive model seeks to focus on the understanding of the nature of the problem and its solution through a systematic approach. To capture the essential features of the two models, the design process may be viewed as a five-step process. The steps are need recognition, problem analysis, conceptual design, embodiment design, and detailed design. These steps and the associated design activities are shown in Figure 5.1 The details of these steps are discussed in the rest of this chapter.

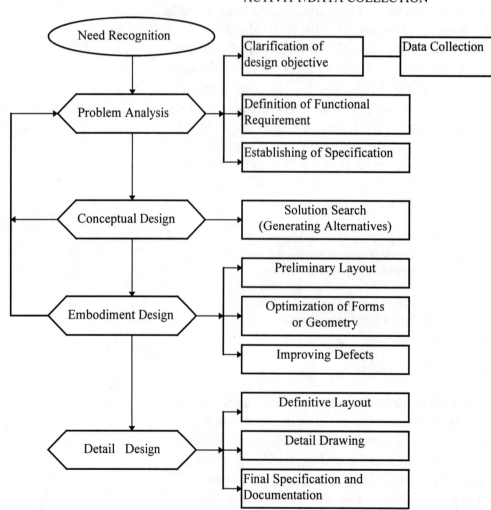

Figure 5.1 The Design Process

5.2 RECOGNITION OF A NEED

Recognition of a need, which is the first step in the design process, originates from many sources. Perhaps the greatest sources of needs are government agencies, such as the Defense Department, which may desire up-to-date military equipment. Needs can be as simple as a self-propelled wheel chair and as complex as a defense system against a missile.

Generally, the need is usually recognized by someone other than the engineer. It is possible that in a big corporation the need may be stated by the marketing division after an extensive market survey. The point is that it is not always the engineer who originates the problems, however, it is the engineer who must provide the solution. An example of need is stated below:

Problem Statement

Design student's desk which is convenient, comfortable and inexpensive.

Addressing an established need requires some specifications. Specifications may include physical and functional requirements and economic constraints. Since no design process can begin without establishing the problem, it is important that the problem be properly defined.

5.3 PROBLEM ANALYSIS

Many individuals who rush to find a solution of a problem often discover that they are solving the wrong problem. A fundamental step in solving any problem is to understand the problem. The process of understanding a problem comes from an in depth analysis of the problem. In design, the purpose of problem analysis is three-fold: First, to clarify the problem statement; second, to define the functions that are to be met in the design; third, to set up or to clarify limitations or design specifications imposed on the design either from the customers or from other sources.

Needs, in general are stated in vague terms. As an example, consider the statement, "I am hungry." This is an expression of need. This statement can have several meanings. It could be construed as, bring food to me, or it could mean take me out to eat. If the person who made this statement has been in a very long meeting, it may be a statement to indicate that the meeting ought to end. If the person who made this statement intended for you to take him out for a dinner, but you ordered pizza for this person, have you really met this person's need? It is clear, that for a designer to meet any given need, the objectives of the need must be clarified. This clarification is known as problem definition.

Problem definition should include as much information as possible in relation to the stated need. A complete problem definition should, at least, include sections that deal with a **basic statement of the problem, preliminary requirements, functional requirements** and **performance specification**. The basic statement should be general enough not to inhibit creativity since the purpose of such a statement is not to address the method of solution. After a basic statement of the problem has been stated, additional time must be spent to extract the design objectives in the basic problem statement.

DESIGN REQUIREMENTS

The design requirements should be viewed as design objectives. The basic need expressed in a problem must be translated into design objectives which, when satisfied, meets the stated need. The objectives must be very clear so that there is no confusion or disagreement between the designer and the client whose need is to be met. The design objective may initially be vague but at the end of the problem definition, this vagueness must disappear. Clarifying the design objectives involves asking questions. It is suggested that you apply the "WWH" interrogative system. This means that you should ask the questions, what? why? and how? Start by asking what the statement means. If there are terms that you do not understand, consult dictionaries, especially engineering dictionaries. This should help you determine the underlying objectives behind the problem. You may proceed to question why the objectives are needed and how they may be achieved. In the process of defining the objectives, it is essential that the client be questioned with regard to the objectives. There should be no surprises to the client. The overall objectives must be agreed upon between the designer and the client. In any case, the result of the use of WWH should be a list of design objectives.

To help the designer keep track of the design objectives it is desirable to apply what is called the **objectives tree method.** This method consists of three basic steps. The first step consists of listing the design objectives that resulted from the use of the WWH approach. In the second step, these objectives are ordered in a hierarchical manner from top level objectives to low level objects. The final step involves drawing an objective tree showing the relationship or interconnection between each objectives. An example that illustrates the concept is presented at the end of this section.

FUNCTIONAL REQUIREMENTS

Once the objectives have been clarified the designer must engage in another activity that is very closely related to the objectives identified. This activity requires that the designer understand the functions desired in the objectives to develop the functional requirements of the design. The definition of functional requirement is not concerned with how to arrive at the desired goal, but with what must be accomplished in order to achieve the desired goal. To make the point clear consider the statement, " I cannot see the words properly when I am reading." Assume that this is considered as a need for which the objective is "to see." A functional requirement may be stated as "to improve eye sight." There are at least two solutions: have surgery or get reading glasses. If you stated that the functional requirement is to use glasses, you have actually provided a solution instead of the desired function. Of course, by so doing, the second alternative solution has been excluded. The person who stated that using glasses is the functional requirement was thinking of how to improve sight instead of what function is required by the objective.

A good way of assuring that the designer has actually stated the functional requirement is to consider the question: given an input, what verb can be associated with it to produce the desired result? (see Figure 5.2.) For example, in the illustration above the input is poor vision and the verb "improve" used with it results in improved vision as the functional requirement. The question of how to achieve the requirement must, at this level, be regarded as a black box that contains all the necessary functions required to convert a given input to a desired output.

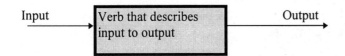

Figure 5.2 A functional requirement model

PERFORMANCE SPECIFICATION

There are basic limitations that must be considered during the design process. These limitations are essential for successful design of a product. The limitations may be due to cost, performance requirement, or other factors that the designer has no control over, such as laws or codes. This set of limitations constitutes the performance specification of the product. The development of performance specification must be carefully carried out since it serves several purposes. It is used during the design process to evaluate proposed solutions. It defines the solution space for the design problem as well. Consequently, a faulty specification may pose serious problems to the designer in that there is no latitude for obtaining a satisfactory solution.

To develop a performance specification several factors must be considered. First, consideration must be given to the nature of possible solutions. This may involve considering the possible alternatives and the features of the product. Second, the desired attributes of the product are to be considered and must be stated in such a way that it does not exclude any particular solution. The attributes should be a list of conditions that the design must satisfy. Finally, the performance specification is developed by stating concisely what the product must do.

EXAMPLE 5.1

Let us apply what has been said about problem definition to the problem statement regarding the student's desk.

I. Establishing Design Objectives

To establish the design objectives it is necessary to ask the following questions:

1. What is the purpose of the desk: study, computer work space?
2. Is it for a class room or a dormitory?
3. Is the desk also to be used by a handicapped person?
4. What does "convenient" mean?
   a. Is it easy to move about? If so, how?
   b. Spacious enough to contain a computer?
   c. Should it be fitted with a reading light?
5. What does "comfort" mean?
   a. Does it mean adjustable ? If so, why?
   b. Could it mean that it should have a means of warming the feet in cold seasons? If so, how?

6. What does "inexpensive" mean?

Answers to these questions may result in an objective tree similar to that shown in Figure 5.3. It should be noted that the objective tree shown is not unique. Different designers may obtain different objective trees. The problem may

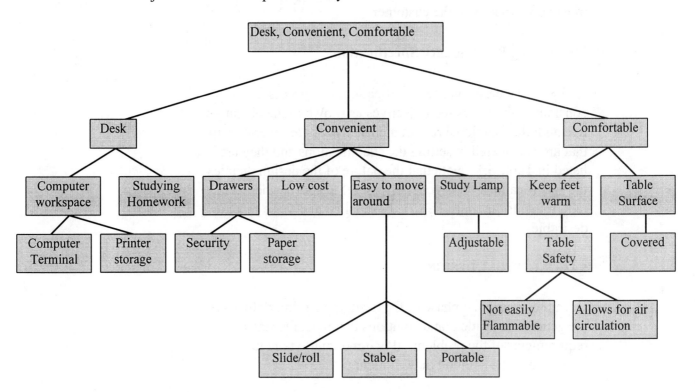

Figure 5.3 Objective Tree for the desk design

now be stated as:

Design a study desk that allows space for a computer and its peripherals; that is portable and can slide over the floor easily; that is nonflammable; that has a lamp space; and that comes at an affordable price.

II. Determining the Functional Requirement

On establishing the design objectives we now analyze them to understand what functional requirements must be satisfied. The functions that are required are listed below.

1. Provide a space for study and placement of computer and peripherals,
2. Supports a study lamp,
3. Slides easily over the floor,
4. Is not flammable,

5. Keeps the feet warm in the winter period,

6. Provides storage space.

The fifth requirement may be viewed as optional depending on the limit price that is set on the desk. It may turn out that it is not economical to include it as a functional requirement. This must be verified with the customer.

III. Setting Performance Specification

To set the performance specification, it is necessary to consider both the desired objectives as shown in the objective tree and the functional requirements. There are several factors that are considered in setting the specifications and they are listed in Table 5.1. Note that the nature of the design dictates the specifications. It is generally useful to specify the requirements that must be strictly satisfied and those that are desirable.

5.4 CONCEPTUAL DESIGN

In the conceptual phase of the design, the primary focus is the generation of ideas and solutions that meet the stated requirements of the problem. It is important to note that a concept may be a notion or a thought.

Table 5. 1 Performance specification for study desk

Item	Required	Desirable
1. Geometry Requirement		
Desk surface area : $0.75m^2$	x	
Height : 760 mm	x	
2. Mass : ≤ 120 Kg	x	
3. Cost $< \$200$	x	
4. Top Surface		
Smooth finish	x	
5. Material		
Wood		
6. General Characteristics		
Three (3) drawers		x
Locks		x
Foot warmer		x

Therefore, conceptual design refers to the expression of an idea or ideas either in words or with sketches that represent the totality of the design. In general, there are two main activities of this phase: generation of ideas or solutions, and their evaluation.

GENERATION OF SOLUTION IDEAS

Generation of ideas or solutions is one of the most important design activities. At this stage, creativity comes into play. One pitfall of this process is that too often the inexperienced designer believes that it is necessary to create novel products when modification of an existing product may be the most beneficial approach. When generating ideas, it is essential that obvious solutions not be overlooked in favor of some unworkable but esoteric idea. It is advisable to generate as many solutions as possible because the more solutions you generate, the better your chances of obtaining a desirable one. Avoid the temptation of going with the first idea that comes to you. Considerable amount of time should be spent in generating solutions. Enough research should be conducted to determine whether similar products or designs already exist. This is an essential step that saves you the problem of re-inventing the wheel. Moreover, if a similar design or product exists it is easier to study the problems of the existing design than perhaps to come up with a new design. After extensive research, the generation of solutions should start. There are several methods for enhancing generation of solution ideas. Two of these methods are briefly discussed, namely, the **brainstorming** and **morphological analysis**.

Brainstorming is a method of generating ideas or solution techniques that involves a group. The underlying belief is that ideas generated in groups are generally better than what may be obtained from an individual. Furthermore, it is believed that sharing solution ideas stimulates more solution ideas. This method can lead to no solution being achieved if it is done in a haphazard manner. However, if the method is properly carried out, it can be very effective. There are certain approaches that should be taken. First, there should be a leader of the group who is to maintain good records of the meetings and ideas generated. The leader must be a good moderator insuring that discussions are focused. Otherwise, people who like to talk can go off on a tangent expressing opinions that have nothing to do with the problem. Of course, the leader must be very tactical so that members of the group are not allowed to judge ideas in the generation phase. The leader must also stimulate the thinking of other members of the group by asking provocative questions. Second, the group should consist of individuals with diverse backgrounds and experiences. Third, each member should complete independent research prior to group meetings. It is very important that the sessions not last too long, generally not more than a half hour, and that the meeting environment be relaxed so that each individual is free to introduce his ideas. Since the groups should generally be diverse, suggestions from non-technical members may stimulate the thinking of the technically minded members of the group. What must be emphasized is that the brainstorming stage is not the time to evaluate ideas. Evaluation is reserved for later. Finally, it can not be emphasized enough that the team must maintain some form of discipline to remain focused, otherwise, several sessions may actually be a waste of time and no meaningful results can be achieved.

The morphological analysis is a method of generating alternative design solutions. It helps the designer to broaden the domain of the search for potential new solutions. The emphasis in morphological analysis is the determination of the form or shape of the product being designed. To help organize the analysis, charts are often used to list the various alternative solutions. By combining the various alternatives, an acceptable solution may be found. Four steps for conducting morphological analysis have been given by Cross (1989). The first step is to list the features or functions that are essential to the product; then indicate the means of accomplishing each listed function or feature. Using this information, a chart is drawn containing all the possible solutions. Finally, using the chart, a set of all feasible solutions is developed. It should be noted that the means of accomplishing a specified function can either be written in words or represented with sketches. An example of a morphological chart for the design of the desk is shown in Table 5.2. Alternatively, the morphological charts, in the form of sketches, for the top and bottom of the proposed desk are shown in Figures 5.4 and 5.5. Using these the designer can select the combinations necessary to satisfy the design requirements.

Table 5.2 Morphological chart for the desk design

Function or Characteristic	Method A	Method B
Study space	flat space	retractable
Store Computer/Printer	flat surface	built up space
Study lamp	integrated	special support
easy movement	rollers	basic four legs
Shade light	enclosure	lamp shade
Warm feet*	heater	rug on sides of legs

* = this function may be neglected due to cost

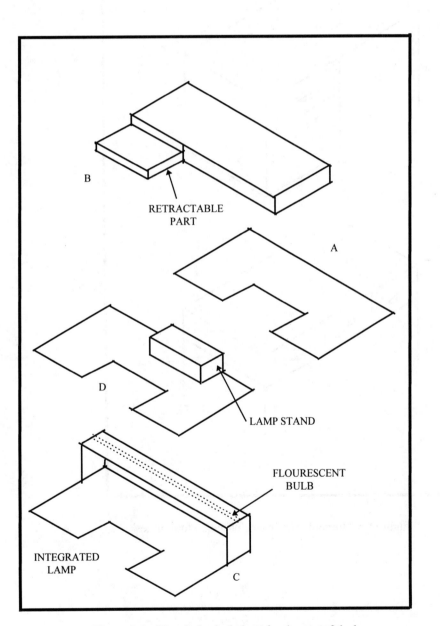

Figure 5.4   Morphological chart for the top of desk

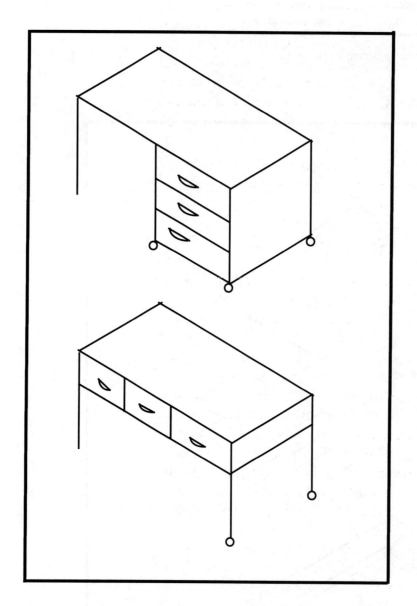

Figure 5.5 Morphological chart for the bottom of desk

5.5 EMBODIMENT DESIGN

At the completion of the conceptual phase, the designer may proceed to the embodiment design. There are those who feel that the embodiment design is a subset of the conceptual design. Regardless of the view one holds, one thing is certain, the embodiment design is an essential part of design. During this process, the layout and the forms of the product are determined. The alternative generated in the conceptual phase are evaluated. The determination of the best layout or form is also performed by what is normally known as **optimization** (see Chapter 11). An improvement may also be made to the selected design concept.

To evaluate the concepts, it is essential to make sketches of the proposed solutions. The first step in the evaluation of the alternate solutions is to list the design objectives from the objective tree. It may be useful to weight the objectives, although this approach may be somewhat subjective since it may be difficult to assess the relative importance of each objective in the overall design of the product. Ideas that do not meet the objectives should be discarded. Occasionally, it is possible to find alternatives that have very desirable attributes but do not meet the stated objectives. If this is the case, the objective may have to be modified or the idea may be combined with another solution to make it acceptable. Some designers use a matrix to help organize the evaluation process. The idea is basically that numerical values are assigned to the objectives and each generated alternative is assigned a numerical number that shows the satisfaction of the objective. The numbers are then tallied and the concept with the highest number of points is usually selected. Regardless of how this process is followed, the important thing is that the evaluation be performed in such a way that permits all the alternative solutions to be subjected to the same evaluation criteria. It is possible that additional criteria may be considered. Such criteria may involve the cost of manufacture, ease of assembly of parts, appearance, or delivery time.

During the evaluation, it may become necessary to carry out an analysis of the forces acting on the product. The strength of the various components of the product must be considered. Computer software packages are available for force or stress analysis. These may be used where applicable.

Another important activity of the embodiment design phase is the improvement of the design. Once an idea has been selected, it becomes necessary to examine means of improving the design. The improvement is necessary to reduce the manufacturing cost and hence reduce the purchase price of the product. One way of improving the design is to carry out an optimization process. The essential functions of the product are captured and an attempt is made to improve the functions in the most cost effective way. The geometry size may be reduced to the most acceptable value that still satisfies the desired function. Other objectives could also include a reduction in the weight or a minimization of wear or an increase in the reliability of the product. In either case, the improvement of the selected ideas must be completed before a detailed design phase.

5.6 DETAIL DESIGN

The detail design phase is primarily concerned with the design of the components that make up the whole system being designed. It is here that the final layout of the system along with the subsystems are presented. Final dimensions of the various components are given and materials for construction or fabrication are specified. In short, all the drawings and production documents are created in this stage. A final review of the design is carried out. Review is essential since any mistake not detected may prove costly in the production stage. The designer must assure that all the functional requirements have been satisfied and that none of the constraints have been violated. All other considerations such as aesthetics must be checked at this phase.

It is important to bear in mind that, in detailed design of components, it may become necessary to establish component design specification to guard the designer from going astray from the overall objective of the design. Great care must be exercised to insure that the various components interface with each other in such a way that the functionality of the product is maintained. In fact, at this phase, it may be necessary to combine parts to reduce assembly cost. On the other hand, it may also be necessary to combine functions, should it be deemed necessary.

The designer must bear in mind that this is the phase in which all information necessary to produce the design is supplied. As such, it can not be emphasized enough that the design should be checked and rechecked for complete production information such as types of surface finish, tolerances and other information without which, the manufacturing of the product could not proceed.

SOURCES USED

Cross, N. **Engineering Design Methods**, John Wiley, New York, 1989.

Pugh, S. **Integrated Methods For Successful Product Engineering,** Addison-Wesley, Reading Massachusetts, 1990.

Walton, J. **Engineering Design: From Art to Practice**, West Publishing, St. Paul, MN, 1990.

PROBLEMS

* In all projects draw the objective tree

5.1 Design an electronic mouse trap.

5.2 In public rest rooms too much toilet tissue is wasted. Design a device that can be used to reduce this waste.

5.3 When people come in a room from the rain, it is difficult to get the water droplets out of the umbrella. Either redesign an existing umbrella to solve this problem or design an entirely new umbrella.

5.4 There are many can crushers in the market. Modify or design a can crusher that is inexpensive, simple to use and uses minimum possible space.

5.5 Design an economical air freshener that is solar powered and can be used in houses as well as in automobiles.

5.6 Many people dislike raking the leaves during the fall season. Design a raking device that is easy to use thereby reducing physical stress. In addition it should be inexpensive and should be easy to store without taking too much space.

5.7 A small business woman makes small "Tea- cakes" that are served in restaurants. The cake contains pecans. The problem is that some of the cakes contain less pecans than the others. Her desire is to have a device that delivers exactly two pieces of pecan to each baking cup of cake. Design a device that will solve her problem. Bear in mind that she does not want an expensive device.

NOTES

CHAPTER **6**

ANALYSIS - MECHANICAL SYSTEMS

6.1 INTRODUCTION

In the last chapter it was noted that design evaluation involves, among many other activities, the analysis of the forces acting on the various components of a system or product. The product or system may range from simple machines, trusses (found in houses or bridges) to complex structures such as rockets and spacecraft. It is important to understand the concept of mechanical systems as used in this chapter. A **mechanical system** is a body or group of bodies that can be isolated from all other bodies that comprise the system. It may actually be a single body or aggregate of bodies connected together.

This chapter presents an introduction on how to perform force analysis. Furthermore, the reason for determining the forces on a component or a system is introduced with the concept of stresses. Stress is related to the ultimate goal of force analysis which is to select appropriate material and appropriate dimensions for a system or product.

A designer can meet the above goal only if he understands a branch of engineering science called **mechanics**. Mechanics is concerned with the state of rest or motion of bodies under the action of forces. The field of mechanics is very broad. This introduction is only concerned with what is called **rigid-body** mechanics because it is the basis for the analysis of many types of mechanical and structural devices encountered in engineering.

A **rigid body** is one that does not deform due to the influence of a force system. In reality solid bodies are not rigid, but the deformation experienced by solid bodies are usually so small that they are considered rigid under certain conditions. The areas of interest in rigid body mechanics include **statics**, **dynamics**, **mechanics of materials**. Statics deals primarily with the calculation of external forces acting on bodies at rest or moving with a constant velocity. Dynamics is concerned with the accelerated motion of bodies due to unbalanced forces. Mechanics of materials deals with the internal stresses and strains of bodies as a result of external forces. This chapter introduces the student to the areas of statics and mechanics of materials.

6.2 SCALARS AND VECTORS

The physical quantities encountered in mechanics are generally expressed mathematically by the use of scalars and vectors. A **scalar** is a physical quantity that has only magnitude and no direction. This includes such quantities as length, volume, mass, speed and time. A **vector**, on the other hand, is a physical quantity that must be specified by both magnitude and direction. Examples of vectors include forces, moments, velocity, displacement, and acceleration. In the remainder of this chapter a vector is represented by a boldface type such as **A**.

VECTOR PROPERTIES AND OPERATIONS

Two vectors **A** and **B** are equal if the magnitudes of **A** and **B** are equal (i.e. A = B) and they act along the same parallel direction. All three vectors shown in Figure 6.1 are all equal even though they have different starting points.

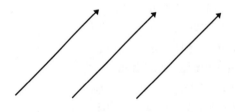

Figure 6.1 Vectors

Vectors must obey the **parallelogram law of addition**. This states that two vectors A_1 and A_2 can be replaced by their equivalent **A**, which is the diagonal of the parallelogram formed by A_1 and A_2 as its two sides. (See Figure 6.2.) The resultant **A** is independent of the order of the addition. This is known as the **commutative law of addition** that is

$$A_1 + A_2 = A_2 + A_1 \qquad (6.1)$$

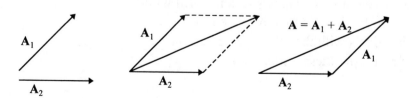

Figure 6.2 Addition of two vectors

The **associative law of addition** (see Figure 6.3) also applies to vectors. This means that if three or more vectors are added

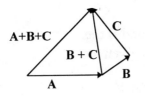

Figure 6.3 Associative Law in vectors

together the resultant is independent of how the individual vectors are grouped together that is

$$(A + B) + C = A + (B + C) \qquad (6.2)$$

The **negative of a vector** is the vector that when added to the original vector gives a resultant of zero. The negative of A_1 is $-A_1$ since $A_1 + (-A_1) = 0$. The subtraction of vectors is addition of the negative of the vector, thus the operation $A_2 - A_1$ (see Figure 6.4) is:

$$A_2 - A_1 = A_2 + (-A_1) \qquad (6.3)$$

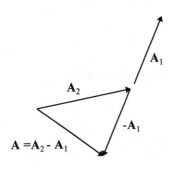

Figure 6.4 Subraction of two vectors

If a vector **A** is multiplied by a scalar k, the product k**A** is a vector that is has the magnitude kA and the same direction as **A.**

Example 6.1

A cyclist travels 10 m along route 1 (see Figure 6.5) and then travels 15 m along route 2. What is the cyclist's total displacement?

Solution

Let the vectors **A** represent the first displacement and **B** the second displacement. Then total displacement, **C**, is given as:

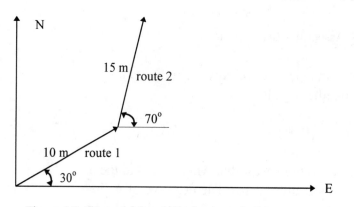

Figure 6.5 Routes of the cyclist in example 6.1

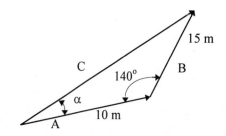

Figure 6.6 Representation of the displacement of Example 6.1

$$C = A + B$$

The magnitude of **C** and its direction can be obtained graphically, but it is more accurate to use the cosine rule. From Figure 6.6:

$$C^2 = A^2 + B^2 - 2abcos\ (140°)$$
$$= 100 + 225 - 2(10)(15)(cos(140°))$$
$$= 554.81$$
$$C = 23.55\ m$$

The direction can now be obtained using the sine rule:

$$\frac{\sin \alpha}{15} = \frac{\sin 140}{23.55}$$

hence $\alpha = \sin^{-1}(0.4094) = 24.17^{o.}$

The displacement has a magnitude 23.55 m and an angle of 54.17° measured from the horizontal in a counter clockwise direction.

COMPONENTS OF VECTORS

The addition of vectors either by graphical method or even the use of cosine and sine rules, as was demonstrated in example 6.1, is not always efficient especially when three or more vectors are involved. A better method uses an approach that involves the addition of **vector components**. To understand this concept, consider the vector A shown in Figure 6.7. The projection of **A** in both the x and y directions, denoted by A_x and A_y, is known as the vector components of **A** because the addition of these components gives the original vector **A**,

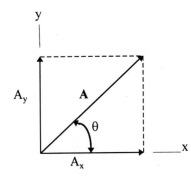

Figure 6.7 Representation of the components of a vector **A**

that is

$$\mathbf{A} = \mathbf{A_x} + \mathbf{A_y} \qquad (6.4)$$

These components are known also as **rectangular components** and by definition of sine and cosine they are related to **A** as follows:

$$A_x = A \cos \theta$$
$$A_y = A \sin \theta \qquad (6.5)$$

From Figure 6.7 it can be shown that

$$A = \sqrt{A_x^2 + A_y^2} \qquad (6.6)$$

and

$$\theta = \tan^{-1} \frac{A_y}{A_x} \qquad (6.7)$$

In order to express any vector in terms of its components with reference to the standard rectangular coordinate system, the concept of **unit vector** is used. A unit vector is a dimensionless quantity with a magnitude of one. To give it directions along the x, y and z axes the symbols **i, j,** and **k** are used. These quantities are known as unit vectors since their magnitude is one. Using this notation equation (6.4) is simply written as:

$$\mathbf{A} = A_x\mathbf{i} + A_y\mathbf{j} \qquad (6.8)$$

Equation (6.8) can be extended to the three dimensional case (see Figure 6.8) as

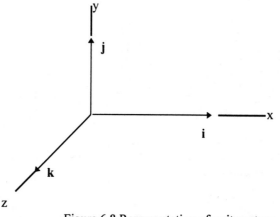

Figure 6.8 Representation of unit vectors

$$\mathbf{A} = A_x\mathbf{i} + A_y\mathbf{j} + A_z\mathbf{k} \qquad (6.9)$$

Note that the sign of a unit vector depends on the direction it depicts. If it is in the negative direction of the coordinate system, it is denoted as a negative unit vector; otherwise, it is designated a positive unit vector. Using either equation (6.8) or (6.9) it is an easy operation to find the sum of two vectors.

Consider two vectors **A** and **B** on an xy plane. The vector **A** is given by (6.8) and **B** is given by

$$\mathbf{B} = B_x\mathbf{i} + B_y\mathbf{j} \qquad (6.10)$$

The sum of the two vectors, **R** = **A** + **B**, is obtained by simply adding the x components together and y components together to obtain

$$\mathbf{R} = (A_x + B_x)\mathbf{i} + (A_y + B_y)\mathbf{j} \qquad (6.11)$$

It follows that the components of the vector **R** can be expressed as

$$R_x = A_x + B_x$$
$$R_y = A_y + B_y \qquad (6.12)$$

hence the magnitude of **R** (see Figure 6.9) is

$$R = \sqrt{R_x^{\,2} + R_y^{\,2}} \qquad (6.13)$$

and the angle θ is computed using

$$\theta = \tan^{-1}\frac{R_y}{R_x} \qquad (6.14)$$

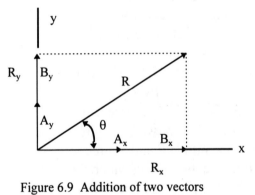

Figure 6.9 Addition of two vectors

Example 6.2

Repeat example 6.1 using the method of vector components

Solution

Referring to Figure 6.5 and by equations (6.5), (6.8):

$$\mathbf{A} = (10\cos 30)\mathbf{i} + (10\sin 30)\mathbf{j}$$

$$B = (15 \cos 70)\mathbf{i} + (15 \sin 70)\mathbf{j}$$

By (6.12)

$$C_x = 8.660 + 5.130 = 13.790$$
$$C_y = 5.000 + 14.095 = 19.095$$
$$C = \sqrt{13.790^2 + 19.095^2} = 23.55$$

And from (6.14)

$$\theta = \tan^{-1} \frac{19.095}{13.790} = 54.16^\circ$$

Note that the same results are obtained, but the angle was computed in a more straight forward manner than in example 6.1.

6.3 FORCES

The concept of force is an important one when dealing with mechanical systems since they are subject to push or pull actions. This pull or push is known as **a force**. Alternatively, a force is the action of one body on another. Consider a case where someone pushes you from the back. The tendency is for you to move forward and not sideways. Also, how much you move depends on the strength of the push. In fact, your movement also depends on the point on which the push is applied. If the push is at your lower back your tendency to move will be different from a push at the head. This shows that a force can be completely specified by its **magnitude**, **direction**, and **point of application**. Therefore, a force is a vector and can be graphically represented as shown in Figure 6.10. Note that the force, **F**, has a magnitude F and a direction. Shown also in Figure 6.10 is the line of action along which the force can be moved without actually changing its effect on the body. Because it is a vector the operations of vectors discussed in the last section apply to any force.

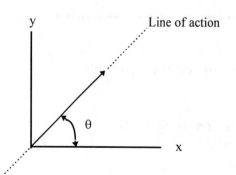

Figure 6.10 Representation of force

Forces that are encountered in mechanical systems are either **contact** or **body** forces. Contact forces result from an actual physical contact between two bodies such as friction force. Body forces, however, are those resulting from remote action,

Figure 6.11 Types of forces acting on a body
(a) concentrated (b) distributed

such as gravitational force. The forces that act on a body may be one of two kinds: concentrated or distributed (see Figure 6.11). The units of force in the SI is the Newton (N) and the pound (lb) in the English system.

To properly apply the operations of vectors to forces it is helpful to classify forces into categories. This classification is either based on the line of action, point of application or plane of action. Forces that act along the same line of action are called **collinear** forces (Figure 6.12a). Forces that pass through the same point in space are called **concurrent** forces (Figure 6.12b). If forces lie in the same plane they are referred to as **coplanar** forces.

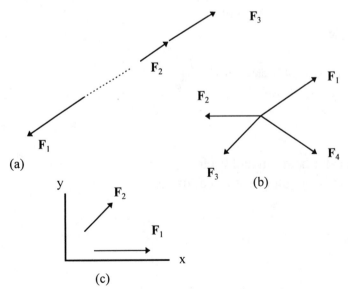

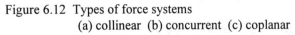

Figure 6.12 Types of force systems
(a) collinear (b) concurrent (c) coplanar

6.4 RESULTANT FORCES

The net sum of the forces acting on a body is known as the **resultant force**. To obtain the resultant of the forces each force is resolved into its components as shown in previous section using equation (6.8). Expressing a force in terms of its components is referred to as the **resolution of forces**. The actual resultant is then obtained by equation (6.11).

Example 6.3

Three forces are applied to a package with a mass 20.9 kg as shown in Figure 6.13a. What is the resultant force on the package?

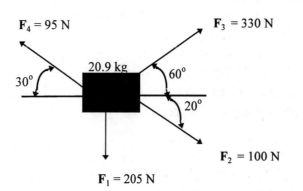

Figure 6.13a Forces on the package of Example 6.3

Solution

The problem is solved using scalar notation and vector notation. The mass is converted into weight (i.e. a force) using Newton's law,

$$F_1 = ma = (20.9 \text{ kg})(9.81 \text{ m/s}^2) = 205 \text{ N}$$

Scalar notation

Each force is resolved into its rectangular component using equation (6.5) (see Figure 6.13b) and the resultant is determined by equation (6.12). This is best carried out as shown in Table 6.1. (Note that forces in the positive x and y axes are positive in their sign.)

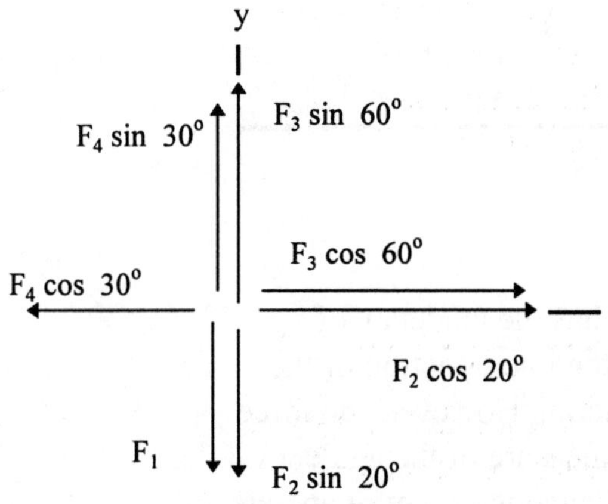

Figure 6.13b Resolution of forces for Example 6.3

Table 6. 1 Scalar solution of Example 6.3

Force (N)	x-component(F_x)	y-component (F_y)
205	0	- 205
100	100 cos 20	- 100 sin 20
330	330 cos 60	330 sin 60
95	- 95 cos 30	95 sin 30

$$R_x = \sum F_x = 0 + 100\cos 20^\circ + 330\cos 60^\circ - 95\cos 30^\circ$$
$$= 0+100(0.93969) + 330(0.5) - 95(0.8660)$$
$$= 176.70 \text{ N}$$
$$R_y = \sum F_y = -205 - 100\sin 20^\circ + 330\sin 60^\circ + 95\sin 30^\circ$$
$$= -205 - 100(0.3420) + 330(0.8660) + 95(0.5)$$
$$= 94.08 \text{ N}$$

$$R = \sqrt{176.70^2 + 94.08^2} = 200.2 \ N$$

From (6.14)
$$\theta = \tan^{-1}(94.08/176.70) = 28.0^\circ.$$

Vector Notation

Each force is expressed in terms of its components (see Figure 6.13b).

$\mathbf{F_1} = - 205 \ \mathbf{j}$
$\mathbf{F_2} = 93.969 \ \mathbf{i} - 34.2 \ \mathbf{j}$
$\mathbf{F_3} = 165 \ \mathbf{i} + 285.780 \ \mathbf{j}$
$\mathbf{F_4} = -82.27 \ \mathbf{i} + 47.50 \ \mathbf{j}$

$$R = F_1 + F_2 + F_3 + F_4 = 176.70\ i + 94.08\ j$$

The resultant and the angles are calculated as in the previous example.

6.5 MOMENTS AND COUPLES

When a force is applied to a body it has the tendency of displacing the body in the direction of the line of action of the applied force. This is known as translation. However, the force can also cause the body to rotate. The measure of the tendency of a force to cause the rotation of a body about a point or an axis is called **moment**. Generally if the rotation is about an axis, the term **torque** is used. Torque is a moment that tends to twist a body about its longitudinal axis. These two concepts are illustrated in Figure 6.14. The force F_1 produces a rotation about the y-axis and its moment is denoted $(M_o)_y$. With reference to threaded element this moment is a torque. On the other hand, the force F_2 produces a moment $(M_o)_z$ and with reference to the handle of the wrench, this is a moment. It tends to rotate the handle in an axis that is normal to the longitudinal axis (z- axis).

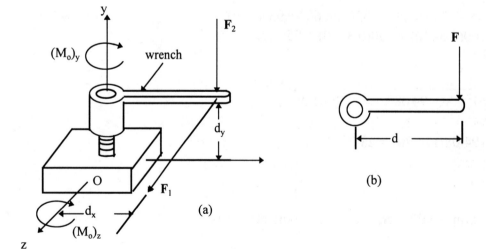

Figure 6.14 (a) Illustration of the concept of moment and torque
(b) Magnitude of moment

The magnitude of a moment, M_o, is determined using the relationship:

$$M_o = Fd \qquad\qquad (6.15)$$

where d, referred to as the **moment arm**, is the perpendicular distance from the axis at point "O" on the line of action of the force. The moment is considered positive if it produces a counter clockwise rotation according to the right hand rule (see Figure 6.15a) and negative if it produces a clockwise rotation. The units of moment are N · m in SI units and lb · ft in English Engineering units.

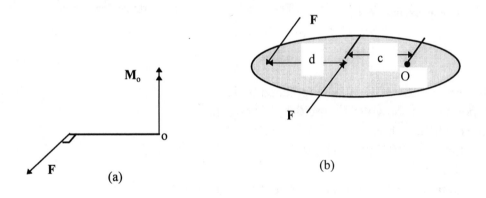

Figure 6.15 (a) Direction of moment
(b) Definition of a couple

The term **couple** refers to the moment produced by two parallel forces that are of equal magnitude but opposite directions (see Figure 6.15b). The net effect of a couple is to produce rotation in a given direction since the resultant force is zero. A couple cannot produce translation. The magnitude of a couple is given by

$$M = Fd \qquad\qquad (6.16)$$

where d is the perpendicular distance between the two forces. Equation (6.16) can be verified by the reader by referring to Figure 6.15b and taking moment about the point O. Applying the right hand rule demonstrates that a couple is always perpendicular to the plane containing the forces that form the couple.

Example 6.4

Determine the moment about A of the beam loaded as shown in Figure 6.16.

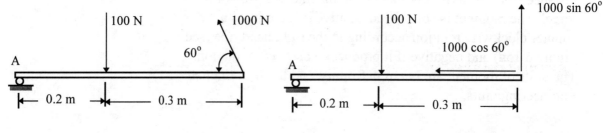

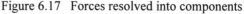

Figure 6.16 Beam loading of Example 6.4   Figure 6.17   Forces resolved into components

Solution

The force with magnitude of 1000 N is replaced by its rectangular components as shown in Figure 6.17. Using the sign convention established above,

$$M_A = - (100)(0.2) + (1000)(\sin 60°)(0.5)$$
$$= + 423.0 \text{ N} \cdot \text{m}$$

Note that the horizontal component has no moment since its line of action passes through A and consequently its moment arm is zero.

6.6 FREE-BODY DIAGRAMS

When a force is applied to a body, that body reacts to the applied force. In order to properly determine this reactive force it is important to isolate this body from all other bodies and to indicate all the forces both applied and reacting on the isolated body. A diagram showing all the forces on the isolated body is known as a **free-body diagram**(FBD). It must be understood from the start that when analyzing a   mechanical system a free-body diagram must be constructed..

The construction of a free-body diagram requires that the types of movement (rotation or translation) that are desired to be prevented by a support be understood. For example, if you are on a skate board, you expect to be free to slide or move freely anywhere over the surface on which you are skating. As a result no reaction or resistance is to be offered in any direction parallel to your skating plane. However, if you attempt to lift off from that plane, you encounter a resistance because you are going against gravitational force and also you are trying to separate the rollers from their contact surface. Therefore, there is a reaction in the vertical direction. A representation of skating board along with its free body diagram is shown in Figure 6.18.

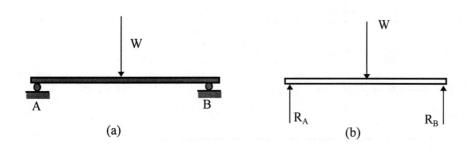

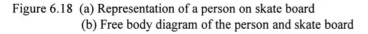

Figure 6.18 (a) Representation of a person on skate board
(b) Free body diagram of the person and skate board

Example 6.5

Construct the free-body diagram for the structure shown in Figure 6.19a.

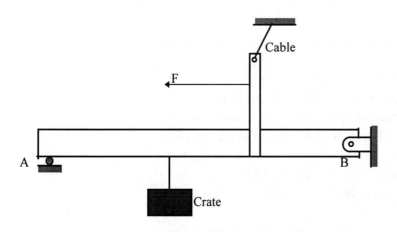

Figure 6.19a Structure for Example 6.4

Solution

Denoting the tension on the cable as T, the free-body diagram is shown in Figure 6.19b. Note that the directions of the reactions can be arbitrary until the problem is solved to determine if the direction selected is correct or not.

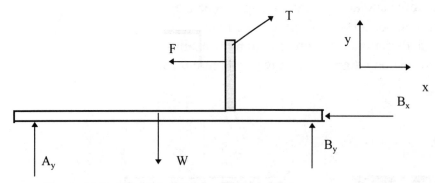

Figure 6.19b Free body diagram of Figure 6.19a

6.7 EQUILIBRIUM

Equilibrium refers to the condition where a body is at rest or is moving with a constant velocity. According to Newton's first law of motion, a body at rest must experience a resultant force of zero. Because a body can be subjected either to translation (by a force) or rotation (by a moment), it follows that for a body to be at rest both the resultant force and the net moment must be zero. These conditions are expressed as:

$$\begin{aligned} \Sigma F_x &= 0 \\ \Sigma F_y &= 0 \\ \Sigma M_o &= 0 \end{aligned} \qquad (6.17)$$

Equation (6.17) is a necessary and sufficient condition for equilibrium because it also satisfies Newton's second law of motion. Newton's second law states that the acceleration of an object is directly proportional to the resultant force on the body. Therefore, if the resultant force on a body is zero, its acceleration is also zero which implies that the body is moving at a constant velocity.

To obtain consistent results in the application of equation (6.17) a sign convention must be established. In this book, the sign convention adopted is that F_x is positive if it acts to the right ($\rightarrow$), F_y is positive if acts upwards ($\uparrow$) and the moment is positive if its rotation is in the counterclockwise direction. Equation (6.17) is the basis for the analysis of bodies at rest.

Example 6.6

An electric utility pole of uniform cross sectional area is held in the position shown in Figure 6.20 by a cable. If the pole has a mass of 284.7 kg and the horizontal surface has been notched to prevent slippage of the pole, what is the tension on the cable? What is the reaction at A?

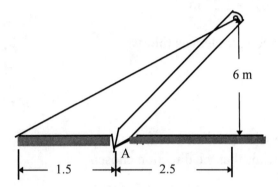

Figure 6.20 Utility pole for Example 6.6

Solution

The first step is to construct the free-body diagram as shown in Figure 6.21. Since mass is not a force, it is converted to a

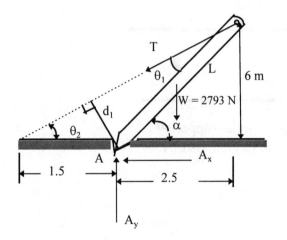

Figure 6.21 Free body diagram for Example 6.6

force using Newton's law

$$W = mg = (284.7 \text{ kg})(9.81 \text{ m/s}^2) = 2\ 793 \text{ N}.$$

This weight is placed at the center of the pole. The geometric quantities shown in the free-body diagram are computed as follows:

$$\alpha = \tan^{-1}(6/2.5) = 67.38°$$
$$\theta_2 = \tan^{-1}(6/4) = 56.31°$$
$$\theta_1 = \alpha - \theta_2 = 11.07°$$
$$L = (6^2 + 2.5^2)^{½} = 6.50 \text{ m}$$
$$d_1 = L \sin\theta_1 = 6.5 \sin 11.07° = 1.25 \text{ m}$$

Next equation (6.17) is applied to the problem as follows:

$\stackrel{+}{\circlearrowleft} \Sigma M_A = T(1.25) - (2\ 793)(2.5/2) = 0$
Solving gives $T = 2\ 793.00$ N
$\rightarrow \Sigma F_x = - T \cos 56.31° - A_x = 0$
Solving $A_x = -1\ 549.27$ N or $A_x = 1\ 549.27$ N $\rightarrow$
Note that the negative sign means that the direction chosen for the reaction should be revised.
$+\uparrow \Sigma F_y = -T \sin\theta_2 - W + A_y = 0$
$= - (2\ 793.00)(\sin 56.31°) - 2\ 793 + A_y = 0$
Solving $A_y = 5\ 116.92$ N $\uparrow$
The magnitude of the reaction is computed as
$A = (A_x^2 + A_y^2)^{½} = (1\ 549.27^2 + 5\ 116.92^2)^{½} = 5\ 346.32$ N
The angle that A makes with the horizontal axis is calculated using (6.14)
$\theta = \tan^{-1}(5\ 116.92/1\ 549.27) = 73.16°$

Example 6.7
Determine the magnitude of the reactions at the supports of the beam shown in Figure 6.22a. The beam has a mass of 15 kg/m.

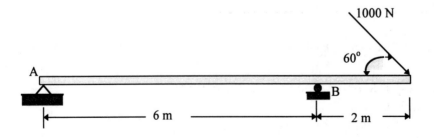

Figure 6.22a   Beam for Example 6.7

Solution

Again, the first step is to draw the free-body diagram for the beam and this is shown in Figure 6.22b. Since the beam has a mass of 15 kg/m, its weight (W) is

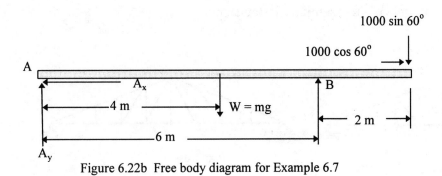

Figure 6.22b Free body diagram for Example 6.7

$$W = (15 \text{ kg/m})(8 \text{ m})(9.81 \text{ m/s}^2) = 1\ 177.2 \text{ N}$$

To determine the reaction at the support B, the condition for equilibrium is applied as follows:

$\curvearrowleft^+ \Sigma M_A = -(1\ 177.2)(4) + (B)(6) - (1\ 000 \sin 60°)(8 \text{ m}) = 0$
   $6B = 11\ 637$
   $B = 1\ 939.50 \text{ N} \uparrow$
   $+ \rightarrow \Sigma F_x = -A_x + 1\ 000 \cos 60°$
   $A_x = 500 \text{ N}$
   $+\uparrow \Sigma F_y = A_y - 1\ 177.2 + 1\ 939.50 - 1000 \sin 60° = 0$
   $A_y = 103.73 \text{ N or } 103.73 \text{ N} \uparrow$
The magnitude of the reaction at A is
   $(500^2 + 103.73^2)^{\frac{1}{2}} = 510.65 \text{ N}$

These examples suggest that to solve problems in statics there are at least three essential steps:
   1. Construction of the free-body diagrams,
   2. Determination of geometry quantities,

3. Application of the conditions for equilibrium.

6.8 TRUSSES AND FRAMES

A **truss** is a structural framework made of slender members that are joined at their ends. The members usually are joined together by either welds or large pins or bolts in such a manner that they form a series of triangles. Typical examples of trusses are found in bridges and roof supports (see Figure 6.23). The treatment of trusses here is limited to **planar** trusses. Planar trusses are those whose members lie essentially in the same plane.

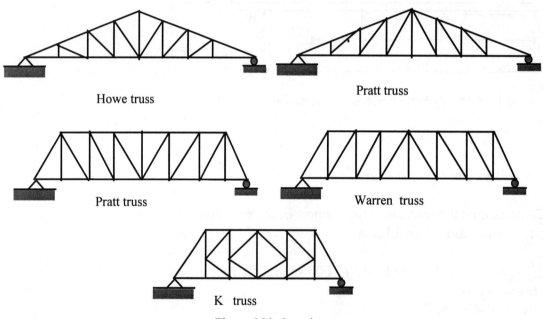

Figure 6.23 Sample trusses

To design a truss simply means to select appropriate structural shape, material and size that can withstand a given loading condition. This in turn requires the determination of the forces in each member of the truss. To determine these forces some assumptions are made. First, it is assumed that all loads and reactions are applied at the joints.   Second, the members are joined by smooth pins. Third, all members are assumed to be straight and each member is a two-force member.   This means that two equal and opposite forces act at both ends and are also collinear.

There are basically two methods of analyzing trusses: **method of joints** and **method of sections**. However, further discussion is limited to the method of joints. The method of joints is based on the fact that the forces on the members on a joint are concurrent and consequently there is no rotation. This leaves the possibility of translation. For equilibrium, equation (6.17) must be satisfied, specifically, $\Sigma F_x = 0$ and $\Sigma F_y = 0$, since $\Sigma M_o = 0$ is automatically satisfied.

The method of joints begins with the construction of the free body diagram at a joint with at least one known force. The joint is identified by a letter and the forces in each member are identified by the letters of the two ends of the member. For example, if the joint is designated as A and a member has one end at joint A and another at joint C, the force on that member is designated F_{AC}. After the force on each member is determined, it is appropriate to indicate whether the member is in compression (C) or in tension (T). (See sec. 6.9 for meanings of compression and tension.)

Example 6.8

A truss is loaded as shown in Figure 6.24a. Determine the forces in each member.

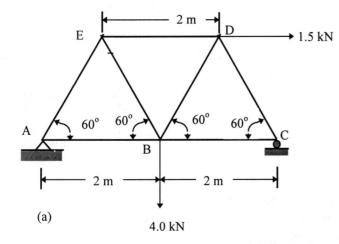
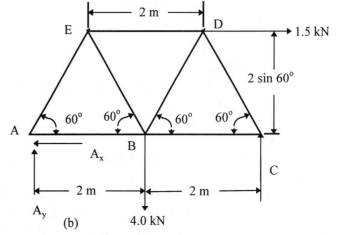

Figure 6.24 (a) Truss for Example 6.8
(b) Free body diagram

Solution

The first step is to determine the reactions at the supports. The free body diagram in Figure 6.24b leads to:

$$\curvearrowright^{+} \Sigma M_A = -(4)(2) + (C)(4) - (1.5)(2 \sin 60°) = 0$$
$$4C = 10.6: C = 2.7 \text{ kN} \uparrow$$
$$+\rightarrow \Sigma F_x = -A_x + 1.5 = 0: A_x = 1.5 \text{ kN} \leftarrow$$
$$+\uparrow \Sigma F_y = A_y - 4 + 2.7 = 0 : A_y = 1.3 \text{ kN} \uparrow$$

88

With the reactions determined, the analysis could proceed either from joint A or C. If a member is in tension it is denoted by "(T)" and if it is in compression it is denoted by "(C)".

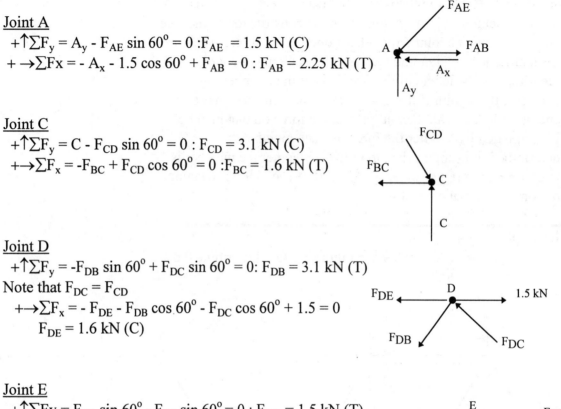

__Joint A__

$+\uparrow\Sigma F_y = A_y - F_{AE} \sin 60^\circ = 0 : F_{AE} = 1.5$ kN (C)

$+\rightarrow\Sigma Fx = -A_x - 1.5 \cos 60^\circ + F_{AB} = 0 : F_{AB} = 2.25$ kN (T)

__Joint C__

$+\uparrow\Sigma F_y = C - F_{CD} \sin 60^\circ = 0 : F_{CD} = 3.1$ kN (C)

$+\rightarrow\Sigma F_x = -F_{BC} + F_{CD} \cos 60^\circ = 0 : F_{BC} = 1.6$ kN (T)

__Joint D__

$+\uparrow\Sigma F_y = -F_{DB} \sin 60^\circ + F_{DC} \sin 60^\circ = 0 : F_{DB} = 3.1$ kN (T)

Note that $F_{DC} = F_{CD}$

$+\rightarrow\Sigma F_x = -F_{DE} - F_{DB} \cos 60^\circ - F_{DC} \cos 60^\circ + 1.5 = 0$

$F_{DE} = 1.6$ kN (C)

__Joint E__

$+\uparrow\Sigma Fy = F_{EA} \sin 60^\circ - F_{EB} \sin 60^\circ = 0 : F_{EB} = 1.5$ kN (T)

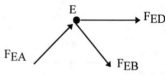

6.9 STRESS AND STRAIN

In the previous sections, the external forces acting on a body were considered. Nothing was said about the internal forces on the body as a result of the external forces. Furthermore, the bodies were considered rigid. This assumption is not always true since forces applied to bodies tend to deform or change their shape. To make you aware of the hidden factors involved in statics, consider a simple scenario of a person being pulled at both arms by two football players with a force of 300 pounds each. If both of these players are pulling in opposite directions, equilibrium conditions insure that the net force on this individual is zero. Can you imagine what this individual is experiencing at the ribs? Yet statics tells us that nothing is actually occurring on this person's body when in fact this person is under great pain. This scenario simply says that equilibrium does not really deal much with the internal forces in a body.

Consider the prismatic bar (one with uniform cross-sectional area) with two equal and opposite forces, F, acting as shown in Figure 6.25. These two forces tend to elongate the rod, therefore, they are known as **tensile forces**. On the other hand,

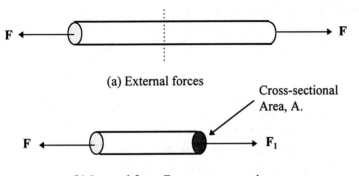

(a) External forces

(b) Internal force F_1 on a cross section

Figure 6.25 Prismatic rod under tension

the forces shown in Figure 6.26, tend to shorten the rod, and are therefore, called **compressive forces**.

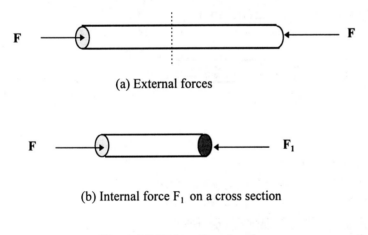

(a) External forces

(b) Internal force F_1 on a cross section

Figure 6.26 Prismatic rod under compression

If a rod is cut by a plane normal to its horizontal axes, it becomes obvious that to maintain equilibrium the force F_1 must act on the cross section (see Figure 6.25b or Figure 6.26b). This force is known as an internal force which resists the external force. In design, it is essential that materials be selected to withstand external applied forces. Since bodies made of the same material may have different areas and subject to different forces, it is essential to have a standard means of comparing the ability of a given material to withstand an applied external load. This is achieved by assuming that each square unit of area of the cross sectional area of the body shares equally in resisting the load. This force per unit area is known as **stress.** Stress is computed using the following relation:

$$\sigma = \frac{F}{A} \qquad (6.18)$$

where,

   σ = stress
   F = applied force
   A = the cross sectional area over which force acts.

The unit of stress in the SI system of units is the Pascal (Pa) and pounds per square inch (psi), in the English Engineering System of units.

   From the preceding discussion, it is quite clear that if there are tensile forces and compressive forces, then there should also be **tensile stress** and **compressive stress.** Both types of stresses are commonly referred as **normal stress** because they act on a plane that is perpendicular (normal) to the direction of the line of action of the applied forces (see Figure 6.27).

   If the line of action of the applied force is parallel to the

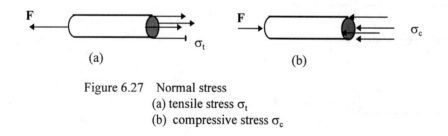

Figure 6.27   Normal stress
            (a) tensile stress σ_t
            (b) compressive stress σ_c

plane of the surface on which it acts, the resultant stress is known as shear stress. This is because this stress tends to slide or shear adjacent planes with respect to each other. The shear stress may be understood by considering two flat plates that are glued together and subjected to two equal and opposite forces as shown in Figure 6.28. The shear stress is computed using:

$$\tau = \frac{F}{A} \qquad (6.19)$$

where,
   τ = the average shear stress
   F = applied force

A = shear area

It was pointed out above that an applied external force has the tendency to deform a body.   This deformation is denoted by δ. The ratio of the deformation to the original length of the

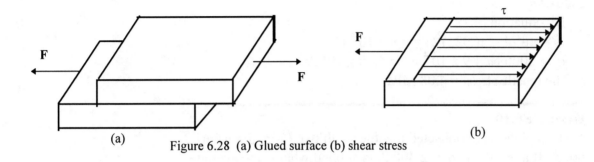

Figure 6.28 (a) Glued surface (b) shear stress

body is known as strain and is denoted by the symbol, ε, given by

$$\varepsilon = \frac{\delta}{l} \qquad (6.20)$$

where

ε = strain

δ = deformation

l = original length

Strain is a dimensionless quantity, however, it is generally expressed as mm/mm or m/m in the S.I. units or in/in in the English Engineering System of units.

There is a definite relationship between the strain and stress in a rigid body.   This relationship is expressed by Hook's law and is given as

$$\sigma = \varepsilon E \qquad (6.21)$$

where,

σ = stress

ε = strain

E = modulus of elasticity

Because strain is dimensionless, the unit of modulus of elasticity is that of stress.

Example 6.9

A force of 2000 N pulls on a rod of 25 mm in diameter. What is the tensile stress on the rod?

Solution

By equation (6.18)
$A = \pi d^2/4 = \pi(.025)^2/4 = 4.9 \times 10^{-4} \, m^2$
$\sigma = 2000 \, N/ \, 4.9 \times 10^{-4} \, m^2 = 4.08 \times 10^6 \, Pa$
The tensile stress = 4.08 MPa

Example 6.10

Two plates are connected together with two ½-in. diameter bolts. If a tensile load of 2 400 lb is applied what is the average shear stress on the bolt?

Solution

The diagram for the plates connection is shown in Figure 6.29. Assume that the load is equally carried by the two bolts, that is each bolt carries 1 200 lbs.

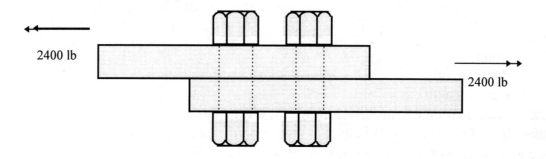

Figure 6.29 Bolted joint for Example 6.10

Using equation (6.19),
$A = \pi \, (0.5)^2/4 = 0.196 \, in^2$
$\tau = 1 \, 200 \, lb/ \, 0.196 \, in^2 = 6 \, 122.4 \, psi$
The shear stress on each bolt is 6 122.4 psi.

6.10 DESIGN STRESS

Engineering design, as previously discussed, is an activity that involves decision making. Some of these decisions may include making certain assumptions about the properties of the material used in the design. Because there are uncertainties connected with the stresses that actually cause a member to fail, mechanical systems in particular are designed at stresses well below their estimated failure stress. Also, because most mathematical models used in engineering design contain some simplifying assumptions, special care is taken to account for these assumptions. To safeguard an element from failing the estimated failure- causing stress for the material of the member is reduced by a predetermined number called the **factor of safety.**

When a failure-causing stress has been reduced by the factor of safety the resulting stress is the **design stress** or **allowable stress.** Allowable stress is the largest stress or the limiting stress that is permissible in a design situation. It is the limit stress that a given material can withstand in service. Thus the allowable stress is related to the failure-causing stress by the factor of safety (F.S.) as follows:

$$F.S. = \frac{Failure - stress}{Allowable\ stress} \qquad (6.22)$$

The concept of design stress is illustrated in the example that follows.

Example 6.11

A tension member is to be designed to resist a load of 50 kN. The length of the member is 2 m long and it should not deform more than 5 mm. The member is made of aluminum with a failure-causing stress of 300 MPa. Determine the diameter of the member. Assume that E = 69 GPa and that a factor of safety of 1.5 is acceptable.

Solution

Given: F = 50 kN, l = 2 m, F.S.= 1.5, δ = .005 m
       Failure- stress = 300 MPa , E = 69 GPa
Sketch:

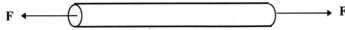

F ← ⊂───────────────────⊃ → F

Find: diameter d

Assumption: member is of uniform cross sectional area

Equations: $A = \pi d^2/4$: $\sigma = F/A$ (eqn. 6.19)

$\delta = \varepsilon l$ (eqn. 6.20): $\sigma = \varepsilon E$ (eqn. 6.21)

F.S. = Failure-stress/allowable stress (eqn. 6.22)

Calculations:

(a) Design against stress:

allowable stress = 300/1.5 = 200 MPa

$A = 50\ 000/200 \times 10^6 = 2.5 \times 10^{-4}\ m^2$

$d = \{(4)(2.5 \times 10^{-4})/\pi\}^{\frac{1}{2}} = 0.018\ m$

(b) Check against excessive deformation

$\delta = \varepsilon l = \sigma l/E$

$= Fl/AE = (50\ 000)(2)/(2.5 \times 10^{-4})(69 \times 10^9)$

$= 0.0058\ m$

Since 0.0058 m > 0.005 m redesign using deformation:

$A = Fl/\delta E$

$= (50\ 000)(2)/(.005)(69 \times 10^9) = 2.9 \times 10^{-4}$

$d = 0.019\ m$

The diameter to be specified is 19 mm.

SOURCES USED

Hibbler, R.C., **Engineering Mechanics- Statics**, Seventh Edition, Prentice Hall, Englewood Cliffs, New Jersey, 1995.

Meriam, J.L. and L.G. Kraige, **Engineering Mechanics**, Third Edition, John Wiley & Sons, Inc., New York, 1992.

Serway, R.A., **Physics: For Scientist & Engineers**, Third Edition, Saunders College Publishing, Philadelphia, 1990.

Spiegel, L and G. E. Limbrunner, **Applied Statics and Strength of Materials,** Merrill, an imprint of Macmillan Publishing Company, New York, 1991.

PROBLEMS

6.1 What is engineering mechanics? If you are interested in motion what part of mechanics would you concentrate?

6.2 What is a rigid body?

6.3 If you are interested in the stresses developed on a body as a result of an applied load, in what part of mechanics would you concentrate your effort?

6.4 Name the two types of forces encountered in the study of mechanical systems.

6.5 Define the following: (a) collinear forces (b) concurrent forces (c) coplanar forces (d) moment (e) strain.

6.6 A vector **A** has a magnitude of 10 units and makes an angle of 60° with the positive x-axis, vector **B** has a magnitude of 6 units and it is on negative y-axis. Find (a)**A+B** (b) **A-B**

6.7 A cyclist traveled 12 km west and 15 km south. Find the magnitude and direction of the resultant displacement vector by   (a) graphical method (b) analytical method.

6.8 Find the resultant of the three concurrent forces shown in Fig.P6.8.

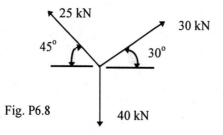

Fig. P6.8

6.9 Determine the magnitude and direction of the resultant of the five forces applied to a ring as shown in Fig.P6.9.

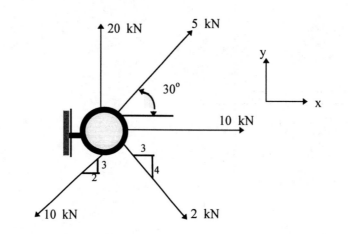

Fig. P6.9

6.10 Determine the angle θ in Fig.P6.10 so that the resultant of the forces will lie on the x-axis. What is the resultant? Is it possible to find an angle for which the resultant will lie on the y-axis?

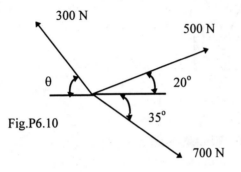

Fig.P6.10

6.11 For the structure shown in Fig.P6.11, find the moment of the 300 N force at the point A.

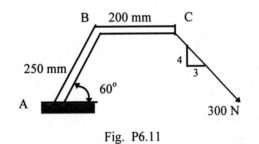

Fig. P6.11

6.12 The L-shaped bracket is acted on by two forces as shown in Fig.P6.12, find the moment of the forces at point A.

Fig.P6.12

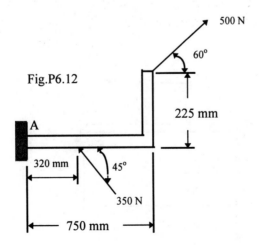

6.13 An advertising board with a mass of 230 kg is suspended by two cables as shown in Fig.P6.13. Find the tension on both cables.

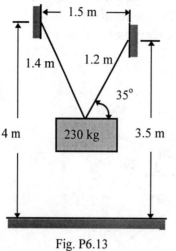

Fig. P6.13

6.14 The bucket of Fig.P6.14 and its contents have a mass of 72 kg. Determine the tension on the cables.

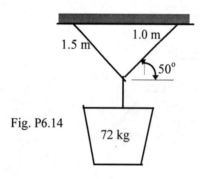

Fig. P6.14

6.15 Determine the reactions at the supports in Fig.P6.15.

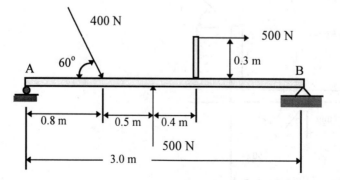

Fig.P6.15

6.16 The beam shown in Fig.P6.16 has a mass of 18.2 kg/m.
What are the reactions at the supports?

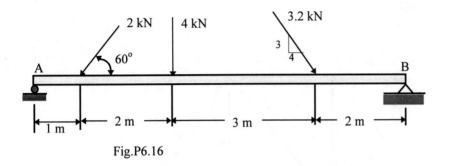

Fig.P6.16

6.17 It is known that the reaction at B for the beam shown in
Fig.P6.17 is 519.8 N and it makes an angle of 33.6° with
the positive x-axis. What is the magnitude and direction
of the force, **F**? What is the reaction at A?

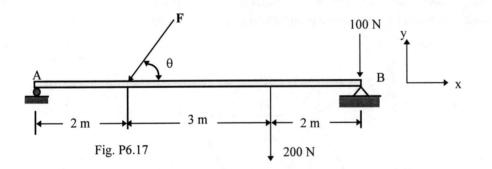

Fig. P6.17

6.18 Calculate the force in each member of the truss shown in
Fig.P6.18. Indicate whether it is in tension or
compression.

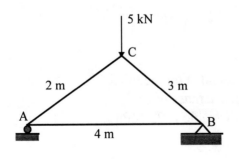

Fig. P6.18

6.19 Determine the force in each member of the loaded truss shown in Fig.P6.19. State whether the member is in tension or compression.

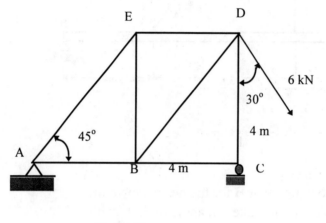

Fig.P6.19

6.20 Find the force on each member of the truss of Fig.P6.20. Indicate whether the member is in tension or compression.

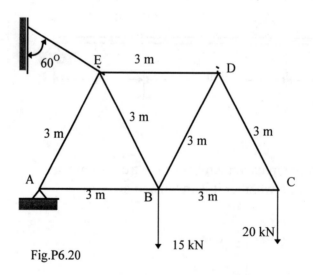

Fig.P6.20

6.21 A beam is pinned at one end and suspended on the other with a cable (see Fig. P6.21). The beam has a mass of 21.5 kg/m. If the permissible tensile stress on the cable is 22 MPa and its modulus of elasticity is 207 GPa.

(a) Find the diameter of the cable.
(b) What is the strain on the cable?
(c) Compute the deformation of the cable.

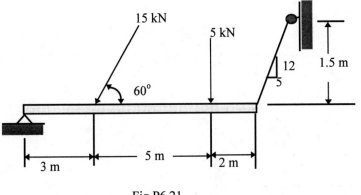

Fig.P6.21

6.22 A short rod is to be used to support a beam carrying two objects of mass 750 kg and 875 kg respectively at each end. If the allowable stress on the rod is 20 MPa, what should be the diameter of the rod?

6.23 Three 20-mm bolts are used to connect two plates (similar to the one shown in Figure 6.29). If axial load applied is 2 kN. What is the shear stress on each bolt assuming that the load is equally carried by the bolts?

NOTES

CHAPTER 7

ANALYSIS - ELECTRICAL SYSTEMS

7.1 INTRODUCTION

Electricity is one of the most useful forms of energy and has improved the standard of living in many parts of the world. The best known common use of it is for illumination. However, it is difficult to conceive of any modern appliance that does not in one way or the other have an electrical part. Many machines consists of electrical and mechanical systems, therefore, engineers must possess a fundamental knowledge of electric circuit analysis. Furthermore, the inter-relationship among various engineering design activities makes it necessary for the engineer to understand the fundamentals of circuit analysis. For example, a mechanical engineer may work with a design team that is concerned with the design of various electronics devices or communication systems. Since the design of electronic devices, power generation and various communication systems depend on the understanding of the basic circuit theory, every engineer should possess the basic knowledge of it.

This chapter introduces the student to the basic concepts and definitions found in circuit theory. The mathematical modeling of electrical circuits is introduced using Ohm's Law and Kirchoff's Law.

7.2 ELECTRIC CURRENT

The concept of current is easily understood by realizing that matter is made of atoms. An atom contains protons and neutrons in its nucleus or central core. Outside the nucleus are found particles of very small mass known as electrons moving in orbit about the nucleus. A proton possesses a positive electric charge and an electron possesses a negative electric charge while the neutron is without an electric charge. Ordinarily an atom is electrically neutral because the negative charge of the electrons balances the positive charge of the protons. Electrons are constantly moving around as atoms collide with each other. This continuous movement of electrons creates what is known as **electric current**. If the movement of electrons is confined to one direction the result is a **direct current**(dc). On the other hand, if the electrons periodically reverse the direction of movement an **alternating current**(ac) results. Direct current is used in such applications as the flashlight while alternating current is the type found in households.

Current is formally defined as the time rate of change of a charge and is given by

$$i = \frac{dq}{dt} \qquad (7.1)$$

where,

i = current
q = charge
t = time.

The basic unit of current is the **ampere** and it is denoted by the capital letter A. Charges can be moved in somewhat organized form instead of its usual random motion by the application of an external force known as **electromotive force** (EMF). Since a force is involved in the movement of the charge, work is done of necessity. This work done in moving a unit charge from one terminal of an element to another is known as **voltage** or **potential difference**. The unit of potential difference in the S.I. unit is joules per coulomb and it is formally known as the **volt** (V); hence, one volt is equivalent to one joule per coulomb.

7.3 ELECTRIC CIRCUITS

An electric circuit is a collection of electrical elements that are connected in some specified manner. A circuit element consists of two terminals as shown in Figure 7.1. A circuit

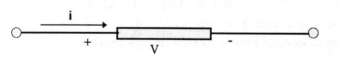

Figure 7.1 Typical element with voltage and current

element is either **active** or **passive**. A passive element is the one for which the total energy delivered to it by the rest of the circuit is always positive. If an element is not passive, it is active. Examples of passive elements are resistors, inductors and capacitors. Active elements include batteries, generators or any other electric devices that require power supplies. Two very important active elements are the **independent voltage source** and the **independent current source**.

A two-terminal element, such as a generator or a battery, that maintains a specified voltage between its terminals is known as an independent voltage source. The voltage is independent of the current through the element. The symbol for representing a voltage source with V volts across its terminals is shown in Figure 7.2 A two-terminal element through which a specified current flows is known as an independent current source and is symbolized as shown in Figure 7.3. The current is independent of the voltage across the element. Independent

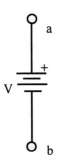

Figure 7.2 Representation for a constant voltage source

Figure 7.3 Representation of an independent current source

sources normally deliver power to an external circuit instead of absorbing it. The power delivered by an independent source may be computed using:

$$P = VI \qquad (7.2)$$

where,
   P = power
   V = voltage across the source
   I = current directed out of the positive terminal

Circuit theory is primarily concerned with **circuit analysis** and **circuit synthesis**. Circuit analysis deals with the determination of an output when an input of current or voltage from an independent source and the circuit is known. Circuit synthesis is concerned with the determination of the circuit when the input and output are known.

Example 7.1
   Find the power supplied by the sources shown in Figure 7.4.

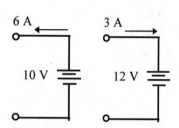

Figure 7.4 Sources for Example 7.1

Solution
   $P = VI$
   (a) $P = (10)(6) = 60$ Watts
   (b) $P = -(12)(3) = -36$ Watts

7.4 RESISTANCE AND OHM'S LAW

   A current flowing through a conductor of electricity encounters a resistance to the flow of electrons. Any device that solely offers a resistance to the flow of current is known as a resistor. A resistor is the simplest and most commonly used circuit element and its circuit symbol is shown in Figure 7.5.

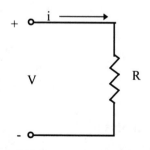

Figure 7.5 Representation of a resistor in a circuit

There is a definite relationship between the current that flows through a conductor and the voltage across the resistor. This was demonstrated by Ohm (1787-1854), a German physicist, and his finding is summarized by what is termed Ohm's Law, in his honor. This states:

The voltage across a resistor is directly proportional to current flowing through it.

The ratio of the voltage across a resistor to the current flowing through it is called resistance.

$$R = V/I \qquad\qquad (7.3)$$

where R is the resistance in Ohms, denoted by the capital Greek letter omega (Ω). Equation (7.3) is, therefore, an expression of Ohm's Law. It is important to recognize that if the voltage is reversed (see Figure 7.6), then Ohm's Law is

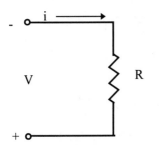

Figure 7.6 Resistor with reverse voltage

written with a negative sign. For example in Figure (7.6), Ohm's Law is simply written as V = - Ri since the current entering the positive terminal is -i.

Example 7.2
   A terminal voltage of 100 V is applied to 5-kΩ resistor. What is the terminal current of the resistor?

Solution
   Rewrite (7.3), $i = V/R$
          $i = 100 / 5\ 000$
            $= 0.02$ A
          $i = 20$ mA

There are two situations that should be noted from equation (7.3). If the resistance is zero ohms, then the voltage is zero. An element to which this situation applies is called a **short circuit.** If on the other hand the resistor has an infinite resistance, the current flowing through the circuit becomes zero. When this is the case the element is known as **open circuit.**

7.5 KIRCHHOFF'S LAW

To analyze any circuit requires the application of Ohms' Law and two laws formulated by the German physicist Gustav Kirchhoff. These laws are known as voltage and current laws. They are applied to the point of connection of two or more circuit elements called a **node.**

Kirchhoff's Laws require a proper understanding of what constitutes a node. A typical node is shown in Figure (7.7).

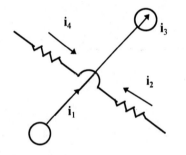

Figure 7.7 A typical node in a circuit

Consider the circuit shown in Figure (7.8). How many nodes

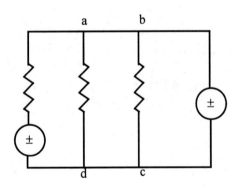

(a)

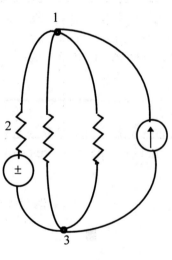

(b)

Figure 7.8 (a) Original circuit
(b) equivalent circuit

can you identify? If you answer is four or more nodes, then you are incorrect. The correct answer is three nodes (see Figure 7.8b). The confusion generally lies with the points labeled a, b, c, and d. Note that points a and b are considered electrically as being an identical point. This is because they are connected by a short circuit (perfect conductor) and therefore, there is no difference in voltage between the two points. A similar situation exists between points c and d. With this understanding the circuit may be redrawn to indicate clearly the three nodes (Figure 7.8b). With this clarification, Kirchhoff's laws are now stated. Kirchhoff's current law (KCL) states that:

The algebraic sum of the currents entering any node is zero.

While the Kirchhoff's voltage law (KVL) states that

The algebraic sum of the voltage around any closed path is zero.

Example 7.3
   Determine the currents i_1, i_2, and i_3 in the circuit shown in Figure (7.9)

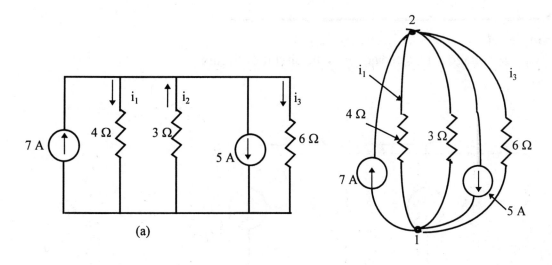

(a)

(b)

Figure 7.9 (a) Original circuit
(b) equivalent circuit for Example 7.3

Solution

Given: two currents and 3 resistors
Find: i_1, i_2, and i_3
Assumption: No energy loss
Equations: $I = V/R$ (Ohm's Law)

$$\sum_{j=1}^{n} I_j = 0 \quad \text{(KCL)}$$

Calculations
There are two nodes as shown in Figure (7.9b). Let the voltage across the two nodes be denoted v.
Node 1: Application of KCL gives
$$7 - i_1 + i_2 - 5 - i_3 = 0 \quad \text{(a)}$$
Let the voltage be denoted by v, then Ohm's Law yields
$$i_1 = v/4, \ i_2 = v/3, \text{ and } i_3 = v/6$$
Substituting in (a) results
$$7 - v/4 + v/3 - 5 - v/6 = 0$$
$$v/12 = 2$$
$$v = 24$$
Hence $i_1 = 24/4 = 6$ A
$i_2 = 24/3 = 8$ A
$i_3 = 24/6 = 4$ A

Example 7.4
Find the voltage across cd shown in the circuit of Figure (7.10).

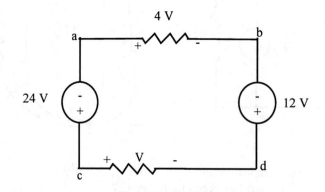

Figure 7.10 Circuit for Example 7.4

Solution

Applying KVL and traversing the circuit in a clockwise direction gives

$$24 + 4 - 12 - v_{cd} = 0$$
$$v_{cd} = 16 \text{ V}$$

7.6 EQUIVALENT RESISTANCE

Resistors in a circuit are connected in two general ways: in **series** or in **parallel.**

SERIES RESISTANCE

Two resistors (or circuit elements) are said to be in series connection if they have one node in common without any other element connected to the node. A series connection is shown in Figure (7.11). Note that elements connected in series have the same current flowing through them. The application of

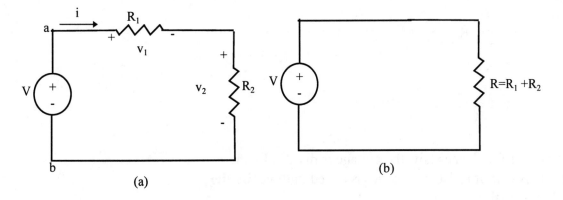

Figure 7.11 (a) circuit in series
(b) equivalent circuit

of Ohm's Law gives:

$$v_1 = R_1 i$$
$$v_2 = R_2 i$$

$$(7.4)$$

Also by KVL,

$$v = v_1 + v_2 = (R_1 + R_2)i \qquad (7.5)$$

From equation (7.5),

$$i = \frac{v}{R_1 + R_2}$$ (7.6)

If the circuit shown in Figure (7.11a) is conceived as having a single resistance, R, between the nodes a and b as shown in Figure (7.11b) then

$$i = \frac{V}{R}$$ (7.7)

By comparing equations (7.6) and (7.7) it is obvious that

$$R = R_1 + R_2$$ (7.8)

In general if n elements are connected in series, the equivalent resistance, R_e, is given by

$$R_e = R_1 + R_2 + \ldots R_n = \sum_{i=1}^{n} R_i$$ (7.9)

A combination of equations (7.4) and (7.6) results in

$$v_1 = \frac{R_1}{R_1 + R_2} V$$

(7.10)

$$v_2 = \frac{R_2}{R_1 + R_2} V$$

Equation (7.10) indicates how the voltage is divided by the resistors. A pair of resistors in series is called **voltage divider**, a result of equation (7.10).

PARALLEL RESISTANCE

Resistors (or circuit elements) are said to be in parallel connection if they are connected to the same pair of nodes, regardless of whatever else is connected to those two nodes. The implication is that elements in parallel have a common voltage applied to them (see Figure 7.12).

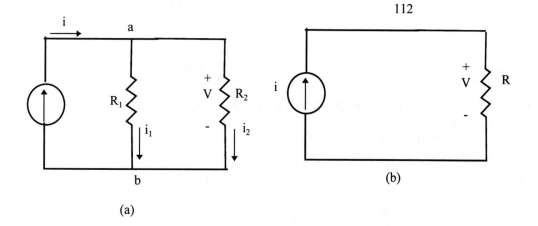

Figure 7. 12 (a) Parallel resistors (b) equivalent circuit

Applying Ohm's Law to Figure (7.12a) and KCL (at node a or node b) gives

$$i = i_1 + i_2 = V/R_1 + V/R_2$$

hence

$$\frac{i}{V} = \frac{1}{R_1} + \frac{1}{R}$$ (7.11)

Consider the equivalent resistance shown in Figure (7.12b), by Ohm's Law

$$\frac{i}{V} = \frac{1}{R}$$ (7.12)

By comparing equations (7.11) and (7.12) it is evident that

$$\frac{1}{R} = \frac{1}{R_1} + \frac{1}{R_2}$$ (7.13)

Equation (7.13) may be expressed as

$$R = \frac{R_1 R_2}{R_1 + R_2}$$ (7.14)

For n parallel resistors equation (7.13) is generalized as

$$\frac{1}{R} = \frac{1}{R_1} + \frac{1}{R_2} + \dots \frac{1}{R_n}$$ (7.15)

Combining equations (7.12) and (7.14) results

$$V = \frac{R_1 R_2}{R_1 + R_2} i \qquad (7.16)$$

Since the same voltage is applied to the two resistors R_1 and R_2, it can be shown that

$$i_1 = \frac{R_2}{R_1 + R_2} i$$

$$(7.17)$$

$$i_2 = \frac{R_1}{R_1 + R_2} i$$

Equation (7.17) indicates how the current is divided in a circuit with two parallel resistors. Because of this, a pair of resistors in parallel is called a **circuit divider**.

Example 7.5

   For the circuit shown in Figure (7.13) determine the current i and the voltage v_1 and v_2.

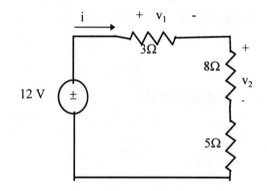

Figure 7.13 Circuit for Example 7.5

Solution

   The equivalent resistance R = 3 + 8 + 5 = 16 Ω
   i = v/R = 12/16 = 0.75 A (Ohm's Law)
   v_1 = (0.75)(3) = 2.25 V
   v_2 = (0.75)(8) = 6 V

Example 7.6

   Given the circuit shown in Figure (7.14), find the current i, the voltages v_1 and v_2.

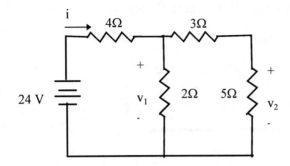

Figure 7.14 Circuit for Example 7.6

Solution

The 3- Ω resistor and the 5- Ω resistors are in series and can be combined into an equivalent resistor, R_1, (see Figure 7.15a). Hence $R_1 = 3 + 5 = 8$ Ω.

The 2- Ω resistor is parallel with R_1 and can be replaced by an equivalent resistor R_2 (see Figure 7.15b).

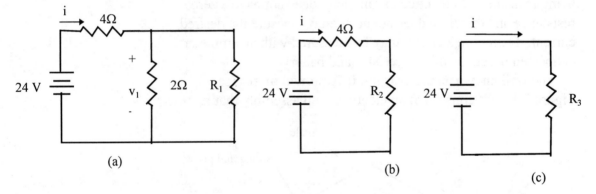

(a)

(b)

(c)

Figure 7.15 Combining resistors

From (7.14)

$$R_2 = \frac{(2)(8)}{2 + 8} = 1.6 \Omega$$

Now R_2 and the 4- Ω resistor can be combined into an equivalent resistance R_3 (see Figure 7.15c), that is

$$R_3 = 4 + 1.6 = 5.6 \ \Omega$$

By Ohm's Law

$$i = 24/5.6 = 4.3 \text{ A}$$

The voltage across the 4- Ω resistor, v_3, is

$$v_3 = (4)(4.3) = 17.2 \text{ V}$$

Applying KVL to the first loop of the circuit in Figure (7.14) gives

$$v_1 + v_3 = 24; \quad v_1 = 24 - 17.2 = 6.8 \text{ V}$$

By equation (7.10)

$$v_2 = \frac{5}{3+5} 6.8 = 4.3 \text{ V}$$

7.7 ELECTRICAL MEASURING INSTRUMENTS

The concept of current and voltage division is used in the design of simple two-terminal measuring instruments. The more ubiquitous instruments are the ammeter, voltmeter and ohmmeter.

AMMETER

An ammeter is a device for measuring current. An ideal ammeter has a zero resistance so as not to alter the current being measured. In practice the ammeter does not have a zero resistance and therefore does not accurately measure the desired current. Current in a circuit may be measured with an ammeter connected in series with the resistor and battery.

The well known ammeter is the **D'Arsonval meter** (see Figure 7.16). It consists of an electrical coil assembly that is

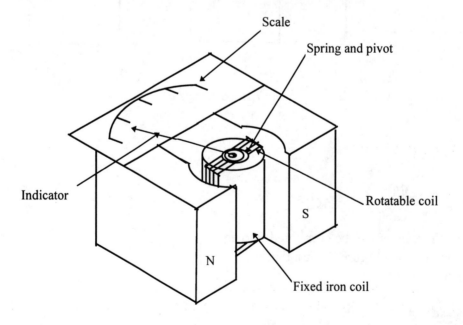

Figure 7.16 D'Arsonval movement

suspended around a stationary iron core placed between a stationary permanent magnet. The coil assembly is connected to two springs that provide an electric connection to the rotating coil. A pointer is attached to the coil for measuring the meter rotation or deflection. The deflection angle is directly proportional to the current in the movable coil and can be determined by using

$$\gamma = KT_s$$

where

γ = angle of deflection of coils
K = rotational compliance of the springs
T_s = spring torque

This instrument is used as a dc ammeter .

VOLTMETER

A voltmeter is a device for measuring the voltage across two terminals. An ideal voltmeter should have a terminal current of zero, that is, its resistance is infinite. The basic D'Arsonval meter can be used as a dc voltmeter by placing a resistance R_s in series with the device as depicted in Figure 7.17.

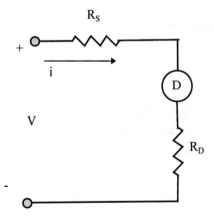

Figure 7.17 Representation of voltmeter circuit

OHMMETER

An ohmmeter is a device for determining an unknown resistance in a circuit. The D'Arsonval movement can be used to determine an unknown resistance, R, by connecting it in series with a resistance R_s and a dc voltage source V_s. The

unknown resistance is connected to the terminals of the
ohmmeter and its value can then be determined (see Figure
7.18). From Figure (7.18) and applying KVL:

$$V_s = (R + R_s + R_D)I$$
resulting in

$$R = V_s/i - (R_s + R_D) \qquad (7.19)$$

What has been described above is an ideal ohmmeter. Actual
ohmmeter is more complex than what has been described, but
the principle is the same.

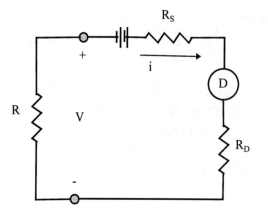

Figure 7.18 Representation of ohmmeter circuit

A meter with a single D'Arsonval movement that is used to
measure multiple ranges of current and voltages is called a
multimeter. The term VOM is applied to a multimeter that is a
combination of voltmeter, ohmmeter and milliammeter.

SOURCES USED

Chapman, S., **Electric Machinery Fundamentals**, McGraw-Hill Book Company, New York, 1985.

Bobrow, L.S., **Fundamentals of Electrical Engineering**, Holt, Rinehart and Winston, Inc., New York, 1985.

Johnson, D.E., J. Hilburn, and J. R. Johnson, **Basic Electric Circuit Analysis,** Fourth Edition, Prentice Hall, Englewood, New Jersey, 1990.

PROBLEMS

7.1 The terminal voltage of 5-kΩ resistor is 40 V. Find (a) the terminal current (b) the minimum wattage of the resistor.

7.2 A 2-MΩ resistor has a minimum wattage of 5 mW. What is its terminal voltage?

7.3 An electric shaver is designed so that it can be plugged into the cigarette lighter of an automobile. It requires 2.5 A when in use. If the shaver has a 11.5-V dc motor, what power must the automobile battery deliver? What size resistor could consume the same power?

7.4 Four 1.5 V batteries in series are required to operate 5.2 W tape player. What is the equivalent circuit resistance?

7.5 For the circuit shown in Fig.P7.5, determine (a) the equivalent resistance (b) the current i (c) power delivered by the 8- Ω resistor.

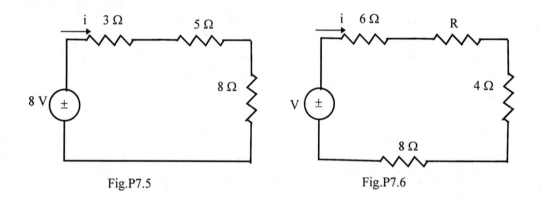

Fig.P7.5   Fig.P7.6

7.6 The power delivered by the source in Fig.P7.6 is 2.5 W. The voltage of the 8-Ω resistor is 0.2 V. Determine (a) the resistance R (b) equivalent resistance (c) the voltage V (d) the current i .

7.7 What is the equivalent resistance for the network shown in Fig.P7.7?

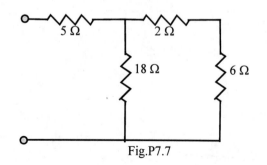

Fig.P7.7

7.8 Compute (a) the current i (b) the voltage across the 24-Ω resistor in Fig.P7.8.

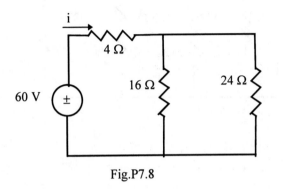

Fig.P7.8

7.9 A load requires 3 A and absorbs 50 W. If only a 2.5 A current source is available, find the required resistance to place in parallel with the load.

7.10 Find the current in the 50 Ω- resistor of Fig.P7.10.

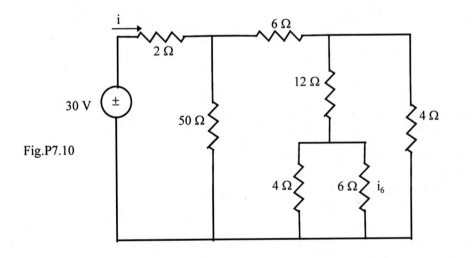

Fig.P7.10

7.11 Determine the current i_6 in Fig.P7.10.

7.12 Compute the power delivered by the source in Fig.P7.12

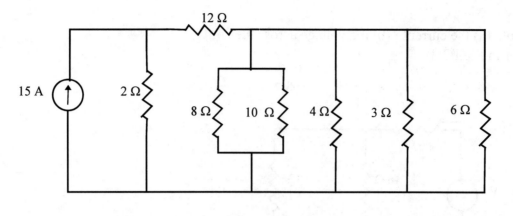

Fig.P7.12

CHAPTER **8**

ANALYSIS - ENERGY SYSTEMS

8.1 INTRODUCTION

Many of the devices that add to our quality of life use energy in one form or the other. Automobiles use energy derived from fuel. Some mechanical systems such as air-conditioners and refrigerators utilize energy in the form of electricity. In fact, energy exists in many different forms. The engineer needs to understand the principles related to the utilization of energy in order to design energy efficient systems or at least contribute in the effort to conserve energy.

What is energy? Energy is defined in several ways. There is no universally accepted definition. This is due in part to the fact that it can not be seen, only its effects are observable. Energy in its simplest definition is **the ability to do work**. Energy exists in different forms that include mechanical energy, electrical energy, chemical energy, thermal energy and nuclear energy. Energy can be transformed from one form to another. For example, in the automobile, the chemical energy of a battery is converted into electrical energy which in turn is converted to mechanical energy that results in the movement of the automobile.

Engineers who are capable of handling various energy related problems are those with basic knowledge in what is called **thermal energy sciences.** These include **thermodynamics, fluid dynamics** and **heat transfer**. Thermodynamics deals with the study of energy transformation and the relationship among the various physical quantities or properties of substances that are affected by these transformations. Fluid dynamics is concerned with the transportation of energy and the resistance to motion related with the flow of fluids. Heat transfer deals with the transfer of energy as a result of temperature difference.

Presented in this chapter are some of the basic concepts involved in the utilization of energy. Such concepts include conservation of mass and conservation of energy. Examples of how the first law of thermodynamics is used in the analysis of mechanical systems are provided.

8.2 CONSERVATION OF MASS

Thermodynamics analysis involves mass flows through a given system. A fundamental law applied to mass flows is known as conservation of mass. *It states that the mass of a system is always a constant.* This means that the rate of change of mass with respect to time is zero, leading to the relationship that the mass flow into a system ($\dot{m}_{in}$) is equal to mass flow out ($\dot{m}_{out}$) of the system. In equation form :

$$\dot{m}_{in} = \dot{m}_{out} \tag{8.1}$$

The mass flow rate is defined in terms of area, density and velocity, that is

$$\dot{m} = \rho A v \tag{8.2}$$

where,

$\dot{m}$ = mass flow rate
ρ = density of fluid
A = area normal to the flow direction
v = velocity.

Example 8.1

A 250 mm inside diameter pipeline is carrying a fluid at a flow rate of 0.16 m^3/s. Due to a reducer in the line the outlet diameter is 125 mm. What is the fluid velocity before and after the reducer?

Solution
The sketch for the problem is shown in Figure 8.1.

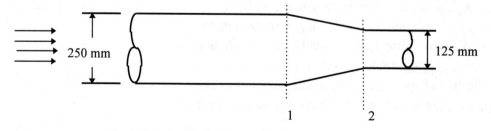

Figure 8.1 Sketch for Example 8.1

Application of (8.1) and (8.2) leads to

$$(\rho Av)_1 = (\rho Av)_2$$

Assuming that the density is constant then

$$(Av)_1 = (Av)_2 = Q$$

The quantity Av is known as the volume flow rate, Q.

$$v_1 = Q/A_1 = (0.16 \text{ m}^3/\text{s})/((\pi)(.250/2 \text{ m})^2)$$
$$= 3.3 \text{ m/s}$$
$$v_2 = Q/A_2 = (0.16 \text{ m}^3/\text{s})/((\pi)(.0625 \text{ m})^2)$$
$$= 13 \text{ m/s}$$

8.3 VARIOUS FORMS OF ENERGY

Energy exists either in a transferred form or in a stored form. The stored forms are potential, kinetic and internal energies. These energy forms can be transferred to or from a system in two ways - heat and work. If the energy transfer is driven by a temperature difference between the system and its environment, the energy transfer is known as **heat**. However, if the energy transfer is driven by any force other than temperature, it is known as **work**. The concept of work, heat and the energy forms are briefly discussed below.

WORK

Work is defined as energy in transition due to any driving force other than temperature difference. This definition implies that work exists in different forms such as electrical or mechanical. The simplest known form is mechanical work. It is defined as the product of a force (F) and the displacement (s) when the force acts in the direction of the displacement, that is:

$$W = Fs \qquad\qquad (8.3)$$

where,

W = work
F = force
s = displacement.

The implication of equation (8.3) is that as long as no displacement is involved no useful work has been done. It is important to recognize this fact since the use of the term work is used differently by the society. For example, the term "work out" may be used in a gymnasium because a person is sweating as a result of applying force against a brick wall that did not move. The person has not performed useful work, although the person's internal energy has been expended.

The unit of work in the SI units is the N·m (J) and foot-pound (ft-lb) in the English units.

HEAT

Heat is energy in transition due to temperature difference only. This definition makes it clear that a body or a system does not contain heat. There is a definite relationship between heat and work and it is given later under the concept of the first law of thermodynamics. The symbol Q is used to represent heat. The units of heat are joule (J) in the SI system of units or British thermal units (Btu) in the English Engineering System of units.

Heat is transferred by three modes: conduction, convection and radiation. The transfer of energy through a body as a result of temperature difference within the body is known as **conduction**. Energy transfer as a result of fluid flow is known as **convection**. Note that there is still a temperature difference. A hot plate cools by this means since the air is the means of carrying away the heat transferred. Energy transfer that does not require a medium such as fluid or solid is known as **radiation**.

STORED ENERGIES

The energy of a body due to its position is known as **potential energy** (PE) and is given by expression

$$PE = mgh \qquad (8.4)$$

where,

PE = potential energy
m = mass of the body
g = acceleration due to gravity
h = height of the body above a given reference.

Equation (8.4) is to be understood in terms of the work done against gravity in raising the body to the given position. The product mg is weight which is a force and h is the displacement. This work transferred is stored in another energy form called potential energy.

As indicated earlier another form of stored energy is **kinetic energy**. It is the energy possessed by a body by virtue of its velocity and it is expressed as:

$$KE = \frac{1}{2}mv^2 \qquad (8.5)$$

where,

KE = kinetic energy

m = mass of the body

v = velocity of the body .

A body consists of molecules. Each molecule possesses potential energy and kinetic energy by virtue of its position and the continuous motion of the molecules. The measure of the potential and kinetic energy of the molecules of a body or a system is known as **internal energy**. It is usually represented by the symbol U. Internal energy can not be measured rather the change of internal energy can be determined using

$$\Delta U = mc\, \Delta T \qquad (8.6)$$

where,

ΔU = change in internal energy

m = mass of the body

c = specific heat (see Table 8.1)

ΔT = temperature change of the body or system.

Table 8.1 Specific heats for selected substances

Substance	kJ/kg K	Btu/lbm R
Air	0.7176	0.1714
Aluminum	0.9630	0.2300
Brick	0.9210	0.2200
Concrete	0.6530	0.1040
Gasoline	2.0930	0.5000
Steel	0.4190	0.1000
Water (liquid)	4.1860	1.0000
Water (vapor)	1.4033	0.3352

Example 8.2

A log of wood was towed for a distance of 50 m by the two forces of 3 kN and 2 kN applied at an angle of 30° and 20° respectively (see Figure 8.2). What is the work done?

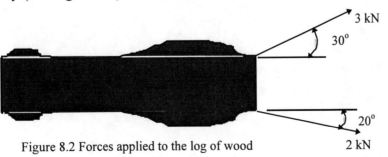

Figure 8.2 Forces applied to the log of wood

Solution

From eqn. (8.3)

W = Fs

The force to be applied is the sum of the horizontal components of the forces since motion is in the horizontal direction, therefore

$F = 3\ 000 \cos 30^{\circ} + 2\ 000 \cos 20^{\circ} = 4\ 477.5$ N

W = (4 477.5 N)(50 m)

= 223 875.0 N·m

= 223 875.0 J

= 0.224 MJ

Example 8.3

If the log of wood in Example 8.2 has a mass of 1 500 kg and the towing took place on a mountain in Colorado which is 1 600 m above the sea level. What kind of energy is possessed by the wood and what is its magnitude?

Solution

Since the wood is at a location above a given datum or reference, the energy possessed is potential energy. Therefore, by equation (8.4)

PE = mgh

$= (1\ 500 \text{ kg})(9.81 \text{ m/s}^2)(1\ 600 \text{ m})$

$= 2.35\ (10^7)\ (\text{kg.m/s}^2)\ \text{m}$

$= 2.35(10^7)\ \text{N m}$

= 23.5 MJ

Example 8.4

A tank containing 120 kg of water at 20°C is heated until the water temperature is 92°C. What is the change in the internal energy of the water?

Solution

By (8.6)

$\Delta U = mc\ \Delta T$

The temperature is converted to absolute temperature by adding 273 to the given temperatures.

From Table 8.1 c = 4 186 J/kg K

ΔT = 365 K - 293 K

= 72 K

Hence
$$\Delta U = (120 \text{ kg})(4\ 186 \text{ J/kg K})(72 \text{ K})$$
$$= 36.2(10^6) \text{ J}$$
$$= 36.2 \text{ MJ}$$

8.4 THE LAWS OF THERMODYNAMICS

Thermodynamics is a science that deals with the study of energy transformations.

THE FIRST LAW OF THERMODYNAMICS

The law of conservation of energy states *that energy can neither be created nor destroyed but only transformed.* The implication of this law is that energy can be transformed from one form to another without loss. However, experimental work has demonstrated that this equivalent is not a one to one conversion, rather there is a definite relationship in the quantitative amount of energy transformed. The first law of thermodynamics is used to generalize the law of conservation of energy. It simply states *that the algebraic sum of all the energy across a system boundary must be equal to the change in the energy of the system.*
It has been previously noted that only two forms of energy (work and heat) are transferred through a system boundary, hence the first law is written as

$$\Delta U = Q - W \tag{8.7}$$

where,
ΔU = change of the internal energy of system
Q = heat transferred
W = work done.

There are variations to equation (8.7) however, when first law is applied as in (8.7), a sign convection is adopted for Q and W. Q is considered positive when heat enters the system and W is positive if work is done by the system.
Equation (8.7) may be further simplified depending on the type of thermodynamic process. There are four commonly encountered thermodynamic processes: **adiabatic, isothermal, isovolumetric** and **isobaric**. An adiabatic process is one in which there is no heat transfer, that is Q is zero in (8.7). Isothermal process is one that occurs at a constant temperature. If the process takes place at a constant volume, then it is said to

be an isovolumetric process. When the process takes place under a constant pressure then it is said to be an isobaric process.

To apply (8.7) requires the understanding of what is known as **thermodynamics system**. A thermodynamics system is any chosen region of space which is bounded by one or more arbitrary geometric surfaces. The bounding surface may be real or imaginary and it can change its shape or size. The region of the space which lies outside the selected region is known as the **surrounding** or **environment** (see Figure 8.3).

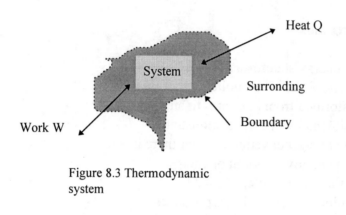

Figure 8.3 Thermodynamic system

Example 8.5

A tank contains 150 kg of water at 20°C. It transfers 2.5 MJ of heat as a result of receiving 8.4 MJ of energy. What is the final temperature of the water?

Solution

The 150 kg of water is taken as the thermodynamic system (see Figure 8.4).

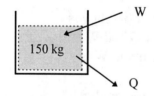

Figure 8. 4 System for Example 8.5

From equation (8.7)

$$\Delta U = Q - W$$

The energy received is work done on the system, therefore

$$W = -8.4 \text{ MJ}$$
$$\Delta U = mc(T_2 - T_1)$$

Using Table 8.1 then:

$$(150 \text{ kg})(4186 \text{ J/kg K})(T_2 - 293) = (-2.5 - (-8.4)) \text{ MJ}$$
$$0.63(10^6)(T_2 - 293) = 5.9 \text{ MJ}$$
$$T_2 = 302.4 \text{ K}$$
$$T_2 = 302.4 - 273 = 29.4 °C.$$

THE SECOND LAW OF THERMODYNAMICS

The first law of thermodynamics deals with conservation of energy during the various transformations. It allows free conversion of energy from one form to another as long as the overall quantity is conserved. It does not provide restrictions to the direction of the processes. Furthermore, there are certain phenomena that cannot be adequately explained by the first law. For example, a cup of coffee will cool to ambient temperature, but a cup of coffee at ambient temperature does not naturally get hotter. To determine the direction of change of processes and also to provide means of measuring the quality of energy, the second law was given. The second law is variously stated, but the most popular ones are **Clausius** and **Kelvin-Planck** statements. Clausius statement says:

It is impossible to construct a device that operates in a cycle and produces no effect other than the transfer of heat from a cooler body to a hotter body.

The Kelvin-Planck statement is as follows:

It is impossible to construct a device that operates in a cycle and produces no effect other than the production of work and exchange of heat with a single reservoir.

These two statements are stated in negative terms and they deal with construction of devices or machines. The first statement is really saying that it is impossible to construct a self-acting machine that can transfer heat from a cooler body to hotter body without being aided by another external device. The second statement, on the other hand, means that no machine can be devised that can continuously transform all of heat supplied to it into work. The implication is that some portion of heat can be transformed into work. That portion of heat that can be transformed into work is called **available energy** and the remaining portion is called **unavailable energy**.

The second law has several applications in engineering practice. One of the most common application of the second law is the **heat engines**. A heat engine is a device that operates continuously and produces work while receiving heat from a high-temperature source and rejecting heat to a low temperature sink. Electric power generating stations use the heat engine (see Figure 8.5) with water as the working fluid. Heat is added to the water in the boiler that turns the water into vapor. The

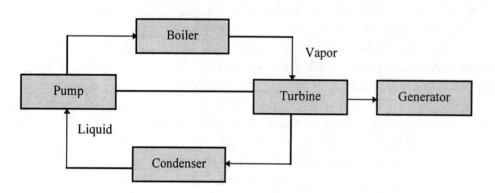

Figure 8.5 Schematic diagram of an electric power generating station

vapor is turned back to liquid at the condenser by transferring heat to a low temperature source. Useful work is produced by the turbine that is used to generate electricity.

Another important use of the second law is in the measure of how much heat is converted into work. This is done using the relation

$$\eta = \frac{W}{Q_H} = \frac{Q_H - Q_L}{Q_H} \tag{8.8}$$

where,

η = thermal efficiency

W = work

Q_H = heat from a high temperature source

Q_L = heat to low temperature source.

Since the second law makes it impossible to create a device that has 100% thermal efficiency, the best ideal engine is called **Carnot engine**. It has the best thermal efficiency that is given as

$$\text{Carnot efficiency} = 1 - \frac{T_L}{T_H} \qquad (8.9)$$

The subscripts refer to low and high temperatures.

Example 8.6

A Carnot engine receives 3.6 MJ/min of heat at a temperature of 727°C and produces 42 kW of power. What is the temperature of the sink?

Solution

The heat received is converted to watts as follows

$3.6(10^6)$ J/min x min/60 sec = 60 kW

From equation (8.8) the Carnot efficiency is

$\eta = W/Q_H = 42/60 = 0.7$

Using equation (8.9)

$0.7 = 1 - T_L/T_H$

$= 1 - T_L/(727 + 273)$

$-0.3 = -T_L/1000$

Hence $T_L = 300$ K $= 17$°C.

SOURCES USED

Janna, W.S., **Introduction to Fluid Mechanics**,
Brooks/Cole Engineering Division, Monterey, California, 1987.

Schmidt, F.W., R. E. Henderson, and C. H. Wolgemuth,
Introduction to Thermal Sciences: Thermodynamics, Fluid Dynamics, Heat Transfer, Second Edition, John Wiley & Sons, Inc., New York, 1993.

Wylen, G. V., R. Sonntag, and C. Borgnakke,
Fundamentals of Classical Thermodynamics, Fourth Edition, John Wiley & Sons, Inc., New York, 1994.

PROBLEMS

8.1 Water is flowing through the pipe in Fig.P8.1 at an average velocity of 2.5 m/s at section 1. If the inside diameters of the pipes at sections 1 and 2 are 50 mm and 100 mm respectively, determine the following:
   (a) the velocity at section 2
   (b) the volume flow rate.

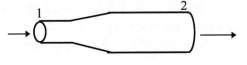

Fig.P8.1

8.2 Crude oil is being pumped through a straight pipe at the rate of 3000 liters per min. If the pipe diameter is 130 mm, what is the average velocity of the oil through the pipe?

8.3 A 130-mm pipe carries 0.056 m³/s of water. The pipe branches into two pipes (Fig.P8.3). If the velocity in the 50-mm pipe is 11.5 m/s, what is the velocity in the 80-mm pipe?

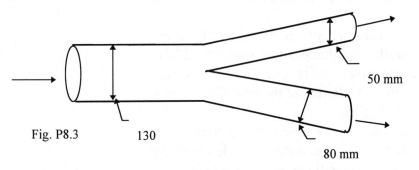

Fig. P8.3   130   50 mm   80 mm

8.4 A heavy equipment is dragged across a rough floor by a constant force of 160 N which makes an angle of 29.3° with the positive x-axis. A frictional force of 15 N impedes the motion. If the equipment is moved through a distance of 2. 7 m:
   (a) Calculate the work done by the 160 N force.
   (b) What is the work done by the frictional force?
   (c) Determine the net work.

8.5 A 120-kg load hangs on a crane at a height of 7.5 m from the ground. What kind of energy is associated with this load? What is its magnitude?

8.6 Heat of 2.2 MJ was applied to 60-kg of water at a temperature of 25°C. The volume of the water was observed to have not changed. What is the temperature of the water?

8.7 Work of 120 kJ done on a closed system resulted in 50 kJ change in the internal energy? What is the heat transferred? Is this heat added or removed?

8.8 Heat of 3 MJ was added to a closed system and 300 kJ of work was done on the system. What is the change in the internal energy of the system?

8.9 A closed system does work of 1.5 MJ resulting in a decrease of 550 kJ in its internal energy. What is the amount of heat transferred? Indicate the direction of heat transfer.

8.10 A cylinder contains 100 kg of a refrigerant. Work of 1.1 MJ was done by the cylinder while transferring 870 kJ to the environment. What is the final temperature of the refrigerant if it was initially at 26°C? Assume that the average specific heat is 0.93 kJ/(kg)(oC).

8.11 Determine the Carnot efficiency of a heat engine operating between 275 and 70°C.

8.12 A Carnot engine dissipates 55% of the heat received from a high temperature source. What is the efficiency of the engine?

8.13 A Carnot engine operates between 70 and 650°C. It is proposed to raise the high-temperature source by 280°C. The alternative is to lower the temperature of the sink. What would be the temperature of the sink if the same efficiency is to be realized?

8.14 A patent applicant claims that a heat engine receives 0.57 MW at 700°C and rejects heat at 200°C while producing 320 kW of power. How will you respond to this applicant?

CHAPTER 9

COMPUTER TOOLS

9.1 INTRODUCTION

Computers are the most ubiquitous device of our modern time. Because of the proliferation of computers, there is the tendency to forget what they are. They are tools that allow us to perform certain tasks much faster. As a tool, it will only perform functions which the user instructs. As important as this tool is, it can not replace the user in doing original designs. Engineers must still come up with ideas and concepts, only then will the computer aid them in rapid evaluation of their ideas. There is no doubt that some of the complex calculations performed today by engineers would not have been possible without the computers. It is impossible to imagine an engineer who wants to be current in today's technological advances without some working knowledge of the computer.

Often engineering students find themselves arguing with their instructors about "solutions" obtained using the computer. They may say to the instructor "that is the answer the computer gave me." The instructor responds "but this makes no sense." The student gets upset with the instructor. What the student does not know at this point is that computer is a tool that does what it is told. In fact, the author prefers to think of a computer as " a faithful dummy." It follows exactly the instruction given to it. Therefore, if the student has given a wrong instruction to the computer the calculation performed by the computer will be wrong. It is therefore important to bear in mind the acronym GIGO, meaning Garbage In Garbage Out. What has been said is: there is the tendency for engineering students to rely on the computer as if its results are infallible. Having sounded this warning to the student, it must be emphasized that the computer is perhaps the most important tool that the engineer uses today. Its applications range from computer -aided design to word processing. The computer consists of both hardware (such as computer terminals, keyboards, printers and plotters) and software. Most engineers are more concerned with the software that aids in their daily engineering activities , especially since engineers often work in a computer-aided design (CAD) environment. The purpose of this chapter is to introduce the reader to the importance of well designed software and the other software tools that are widely used today by engineers to relieve them from some repetitive activities. In addition, a quick summary of some fundamentals necessary to write programs in Q-Basic is presented.

9.2 CHARACTERISTICS OF A GOOD SOFTWARE

Software may be defined as a set of written instructions, procedures, and rules which directs the operation of the computer. The terms software and program have become virtually interchangeable until recently, when the read-only memory chips (ROM) were introduced. Programs that are stored in ROMs are known as **firmware** since these programs can not be altered by the user. Programs on other storage media, such as files are called **software**. But because the programs a student writes are stored in files rather than in ROM chips, the word "software" and "program" are used interchangeably.

It is important to understand what constitutes good software, in order both to develop and to select quality programs.

The characteristics of good software are:

1. Efficiency

An efficient program is one that results in the effective use of the CPU (central processing unit) in terms of both time and storage. Efficient software may be costly to develop. In general, the efficiency of software is related to the size or complexity of the program. A smaller program, if it is well-designed, is likely to be more efficient than a large, complex program.

2. Simplicity

Well-designed software must be very easy to use. This is called "user friendly," or it is said that the user can "interface freely" with the software without any difficulty. The software should be written in a language suitable to the user and it should be easy to learn. If software cannot be easily learned, designers are likely to shy away from it, regardless of its capability.

3. Flexibility

Flexibility is a measure of the degree of difficulty involved in modifying software to conform to a new specification. If software is properly designed, future modifications or changes become very easy. Hence the principle: flexible software requires little maintenance.

4 Readability

Readability is a measure of how easily a user can comprehend the logic behind the software. To make a software readable requires proper documentation of the programming process within the program. Style and aesthetics become important in readability of the program; for instance, it is very helpful to leave as much space as possible between various sections or lines of the program. The program must be free of ambiguities.

5. Portability

Portability has to do with the ease by which a program may be transferred from one system to another. This feature is highly desirable in the area of CAD; unfortunately, some of the application programs in CAD today are machine-dependent.

6. Reliability

Reliability is a measure of the functionality of the software with respect to a desired specification. Reliability is a very important aspect of software design, especially because many processes/operations today which are software-dependent deal with human life. For example, the software that controls the flight of airplanes must be absolutely reliable. If it were to fail, the result could be injuries or the loss of life.

7. Recoverability

A well designed software must not crash (that is, fail to run) because of an error on the part of the user. When the user makes a mistake in the entry of data the software must have a means of warning the user of the error and at the same time continue to function. This characteristic of good software is known as recoverability.

9.3 SOFTWARE DESIGN PROCESS

Before discussing the design process, recall that software is a set of written instructions which directs a computer to operate on a set of given data in order to achieve desired results. Any software consists of three parts: data, algorithm, and structure. The word data as used here represents a set whose members or elements are numerical values, names, symbols, and codes. Algorithm deals with how a set of data should be manipulated. Structure is organization.

Software design is a process of determining how best to instruct the computer to perform a given task. It encompasses every step taken before the actual writing of the necessary instruction in a given computer language.

The design of software can be approached in several steps. For our purpose, the design process consists of four parts: analysis, algorithm design, coding, and testing. Each part is examined in the subsequent sections.

ANALYSIS

Many people write programs which are full of errors and unworkable. One reason for this is the lack of analysis which involves proper identification of the objective. The designer must take time to understand the task to be performed so as to have an unambiguous and complete statement of the problem.

In the analysis stage, the designer must clearly examine the specifications of the software which deal mostly with the input and output of data. Attention should be paid to the sources of data, the input devices, whether keyboard, tapes or other peripherals. The output devices, such as printer, screen or microfilms, should be considered. The input/output devices will affect the manner of writing a program.

Analysis, therefore, is the keystone to a well-designed program. It is the beginning stage for resolution of problems that may be encountered in the coding stage. A good analysis of the task minimizes coding difficulties. The overall plan for the design of software should be properly documented.

In summary, the analysis should result in a layout of the design procedure. This procedure should define the purpose, data (input/output), test cases, and expected results of the test cases (see Figure 9.1).

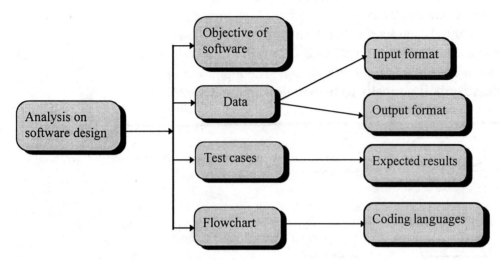

Figure 9.1 Typical result of the analysis stage in a software design process

ALGORITHM DESIGN

As mentioned previously, an algorithm deals with the manipulation of data. Algorithm is defined as an unambiguous set of instructions or executable actions or steps that must be taken in order to solve a particular problem. Therefore, algorithm design involves the development of these instructions in a logical manner, so that the execution of the given instructions results in the solution of the problem. The instructions may be written in English or in what is now called pseudo-language or model programming language. However, the best approach to algorithm design, especially for one not well-experienced in programming, is the use of flow charts. Some features of flow charting are briefly discussed below.

FLOW CHART

Recall that the computer may be thought of as a "faithful dummy" that does exactly what it is told, following precisely and sequentially the instructions issued by the programmer. It has no way of telling if the steps of execution of the program are out of sequence. One way of producing an unambiguous sequence is through the use of flow charts. A flow chart can be viewed as a diagrammatic representation of the sequence of operations to be performed by the computer.

A flow chart is extremely useful when programming in any language. It allows the programmer to detect any logical flaws in the program and hence enhances the logical thinking process during the design phase of a program. A good flow chart should be such that a third party could easily use it to understand the function of a given program. A flow chart consists of symbols and lines called **flow lines**. The various symbols in use are shown in Figure 9.2. Certain characteristics of some of these symbols are worth noting. The input/output and process symbols normally have two flow lines - an entry

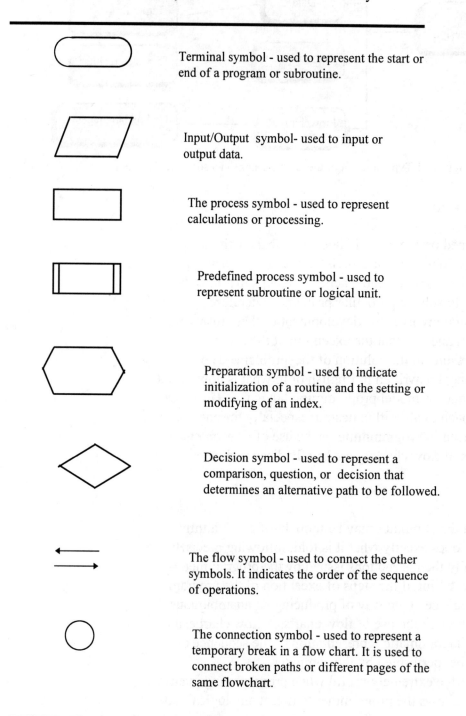

Terminal symbol - used to represent the start or end of a program or subroutine.

Input/Output symbol- used to input or output data.

The process symbol - used to represent calculations or processing.

Predefined process symbol - used to represent subroutine or logical unit.

Preparation symbol - used to indicate initialization of a routine and the setting or modifying of an index.

Decision symbol - used to represent a comparison, question, or decision that determines an alternative path to be followed.

The flow symbol - used to connect the other symbols. It indicates the order of the sequence of operations.

The connection symbol - used to represent a temporary break in a flow chart. It is used to connect broken paths or different pages of the same flowchart.

Figure 9.2 Some standard flowchart symbols.

and an exit.   The terminal symbol has one flow line, either entering into it (if it is at the end of the flow chart) or leaving it (if it is at the start of the flow chart). The decision symbol has one entrance line and a maximum of three exit lines (two are more common). In the use of the decision symbol, it is imperative that no two branches (exit lines) should be equally valid choices, as this may create some confusion in the program or may even result in an erroneous solution.

Since a process symbol has only one entry line, it sometimes becomes necessary to merge the flow lines coming out of the decision symbol into a single line. The point where all the flow lines coming out of the decision box meet is called a **merge point**. There are two ways to represent the merging of the flow lines, shown in Figure 9.3. Under no circumstances should two

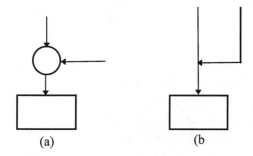

Figure 9.3 Representation of merging flow lines
(a) method 1 (b) method 2

flow lines enter an operation symbol. It is important to realize that once the merge point has been passed one can no longer perform operations which will be applicable to only one of the flow paths. Besides, the merge point makes it easier to do a backwards trace of the flow chart. It is obvious that once a merge point is located in a flow chart, the preceding operations must have been some form of logical operation.

The best way to construct a flow chart is first to view the computer program as consisting of three main phases: input, processing, and output. Then write short statements about each phase in relation to the problem definition. As an illustration, suppose there is the need to construct a flow chart to solve a quadratic equation

$$x \ = \ \frac{-b \ \pm \sqrt{b^2 - 4ac}}{2a}$$

The procedure is as follows:

1. Problem definition:
    Prepare flow chart to solve a quadratic equation .
2. Mathematical equation needed:

$$x = \frac{-b \pm \sqrt{b^2 - 4ac}}{2a}$$

3. Input - a, b, and c.
4. Processing:
    Note that since the square root of a negative
quantity cannot be taken, further decisions are required.
    Three cases arise:
    (a) $b^2 = 4ac$
    (b) $b^2 > 4ac$
    (c) $b^2 < 4ac$

The two cases (a) and (b), can be combined in which case
the decision will result in either computing the root of the
quadratic or not. It is essential to anticipate that it is possible
for some user of the program to mistakenly enter a = 0. If
this were to happen the program should not crash, so an error
message is necessary that will say "This is not a quadratic
equation" or "the values you have entered are not valid for a
quadratic equation."

5. Output: The output may be to print the solution of the
    equation or a statement showing that an imaginary
    solution exists or that there is an error, and then
    terminate the program. The flow chart for this simple
    problem is shown in Figure 9.4.

In summary, flow charts should be used to indicate the flow
of information and the logical relationships between various
components of the software. Besides helping the designer to be
sure that all aspects of the software specifications have been
covered, flow charts help reveal any inconsistencies in the
programming logic.

CODING

Coding deals with the actual writing of the program . At this
phase, the computer language to be used is selected based on the
analysis of the problem. Since the coding phase is essential to
obtaining a functional program, great care must be exercised.

Perhaps one of the best approaches to producing an error free program is the use of structured programming.

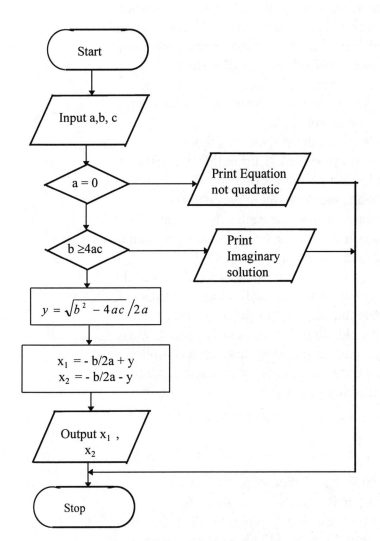

Figure 9.4 Flowchart for solving a quadratic equation

Structured programming is an approach which concentrates on the organization (or structure) and logic involved in designing (or developing) software. The two main parts of structured programming are:

1. Top-down design (Modular programming)
2. Structural coding.

TOP DOWN-DESIGN

In the development of large software packages, many people are involved. Each person is assigned to develop a functional section of the entire program. Finally, the different sections are integrated. This approach would be very difficult were it not for the top down design process, which is defined as the process of dividing a program into smaller sub-units, called modules, which are organized in a hierarchical structure. Hierarchical structural organization means that the first-used module comes first and the last used module comes last.

The process begins with the development of the main program (called the control program). During this, it is assumed that a subprogram for handling complex operations (calculations) exists. When the entire main program is developed, then attention is focused on each subprogram. The advantage of this approach is obvious: one does not get bogged down with details and lose the chain of thought while constructing the control program. It must be noted that even the subprograms may be subdivided into smaller units. The use of the top-down design method helps to develop error free programs, following the old cliché "divide and conquer." It is much easier to solve several simple problems than a complex one. The success of this method depends on the modularization, which can be termed modular programming.

MODULAR PROGRAMMING

Modular programming is a method of partitioning a program into small independent units called **modules**. A module is any collection of executable program statements that forms a closed subprogram, capable of being called from any other part of the program or of being independently compiled. A module can also mean simply a set of statements which are operated on as an entity such as the **IF_THEN_ELSE** described below. A well structured program depends on proper design of the constituent modules. There are several factors that must be considered in module design.

1. Module size

The reason for partitioning of a program is to create a series of manageable-sized programs. Many experienced programmer advocate that the average size of a module should be about 60 lines of code; others contend that the appropriate size should be one page.

2. Module Independence

It is desirable to make each module in the program be as independent as possible. This is useful particularly in eliminating what is called ripple effect, a change in one portion of a program causing a problem in other parts of the program.

STRUCTURED CODING

The importance of coding in software design has already been noted. Any process that results in good coding should be properly examined. Structured coding is one such process which is a highly-structured technique for writing programs. Good programmers do not write programs; rather, they structure programs.

Structured coding is based on the well-known Structure Theorem which states:

> *Any proper program (a program with a single entry line and a single exit line) can be constructed using only three logic structures viz.: **sequence**, **IF THEN ELSE**, and **DO WHILE** constructs.*

While it is true that, at least in theory, a proper program can be written using these three constructs, it is often more practical to include other constructs. The Selection and Repetition constructs are discussed in section 9.5.

TESTING

The final step in producing workable program is testing of the program developed. Testing and debugging go hand in hand, but testing has the primary purpose of verifying that the program executes according to the design specifications. The program must provide correct solutions under all conditions. If a program is well-designed and properly coded, this step can be relatively easy. In fact, it is beneficial to do what is known as a "walk through" which is having another experienced programmer go through your algorithm with some numerical values. This should be done before actual coding begins.

Testing helps to detect at least two classes of errors: logical and specification errors. Logical errors are due to incorrect algorithm design and may manifest themselves in such a way as infinite loops (that is the programming will keep running indefinitely). Specification errors are associated with functional and programming specification; they may be caused by improper or incomplete definitions in a statement line.

There are various methods for testing a program, but this discussion is limited to two approaches: **phased testing** and **incremental testing** . Phased testing tests a group of subprograms (or modules) together. Using this method involves coding and testing each module (subprogram) separately, compiling and linking all modules, and finally running and debugging the modules together. Incremental testing involves first coding and testing each module (or subprogram) separately, then incorporating each into a correctly working program; each newly formed unit is then tested. It should be obvious that incremental testing is preferable to phased testing, since incremental testing makes it easier to detect which module causes an error in the main unit.

Regardless of what method is used, the program must be tested for correctness. This is normally done through input of data which will produce a predetermined solution. If the expected result is not obtained, then it is an indication that the program is not correct and must be modified. Also, the program must be tested to be sure that in each case of a decision process (IF THEN ELSE), each path produces an acceptable result; if a specified data would produce an error, there must be a warning message before the termination of the program. In other words, wrong input should not cause the program to crash.

9.4 PROGRAMMING LANGUAGES

There are many programming languages available. Those commonly used in engineering applications are BASIC, FORTRAN and C. These are known as high-level languages since there is a lower level language known generally as machine language. There are many variations of these three, for example there is the *Quick* , *GW* and *Visual* BASIC. Another level of programming language is the assembly language. It is a complex and tedious programming language. However, it allows one to program in a compact manner and it has a very high speed of execution.

BASIC means Beginners All-Purpose Instruction Code and it was developed at Darthmouth College in the early 1960s. It was designed to be easy to use and learn by students. Since its introduction several modifications have been added to make this a very powerful programming language that is easy to use.

FORTRAN is an acronym for "Formula Translation." It was developed in the mid-1950s specifically for engineering and scientific community and it is a relatively easy to use. Many engineering application programs for mainframe computers is written in FORTRAN.

The C language was developed between 1969 and 1972 at Bell Laboratories. It was written originally for the UNIX operating system. (An operating system is a program that assists in the use of computer's resources.) C is a powerful programming language because it is fast, approaching the speed of an assembly language which is the fastest language. In addition, it is compact. This means that the size of a program written in C is smaller than that of FORTRAN or BASIC. It is probably the most versatile language for writing different types of programs such as operating systems, compilers, and CAD programs.

9.5 PROGRAMMING IN QUICK BASIC

You may ask the question why introduce BASIC programming language instead of the other languages? The most obvious reason is that it is probably the easiest programming language to learn and use. Of course, the more compelling reason is that it is one of the best supported programming languages. It is not only common but it is most frequently developed and most upgraded by the software producers. It is as powerful as most other programming languages in terms of its processing capability.

There are many varieties of BASIC but QUICK BASIC has been chosen for two reasons. First, it comes with MS-DOS (Microsoft Disk Operating System) which most personal computers run. Second, it provides a good programming environment. The term *"good environment"* simply means that the program is written, edited, ran and debugged (removal of errors) all in one on-screen workspace. Second, it allows for structured program and graphics (of course, so does the C-language).

THE Q-BASIC APPROACH

The intention is not to give you all that you need to program in BASIC, but simply to introduce you to some basic ideas that will allow you to write simple programs. Detailed programming guides can be found in the sources listed at the end of this chapter. The approach follows the concept that programming consist of three parts: input, processing, and output. Therefore, the concepts that address these three parts are introduced to enable you to write simple programs. Furthermore, this cursory approach to BASIC programming contains all the elements of the Structure theorem. The layout then is to define certain terms, then learn the syntax for input and output of data and the three constructs in the Structure theorem.

DEFINITIONS

Variables

This is a name that is given to an object. It can be used to represent a numeric value. For example to assign a value of 560.50 in the computer a variable name x may be chosen so that
$$x = 560.50$$
Q-Basic allows the name of any variable to contain up to 40 characters. These characters may be letters, numbers, decimal point and type-declaration characters such as %,$ and #. The rule however is that a variable must begin with a letter. For example it is permissible to give a variable as x22 but not 22x. Also, the variable must **not** be one of the reserved BASIC words (see Appendix D).

Data

Data is any set of information supplied to the computer in order to obtain a desired result. Hence a set of data may consist of numbers, names or symbols. Every variable entered into the computer falls into one of two types of data: numeric or string.

Numeric Data Types

These are number characters. There are two major

types; integer and floating point. Integers are numbers written without decimal points (e.g. 35000), where as floating point numbers are written with decimal points (e.g. 3500.25).

String Data Types

A string is a sequence of characters (alphabetic or numeric) or symbols. A string variable can contain up to 32 767 characters. It is useful in processing of nonnumeric data. Any variable becomes a string when followed by the dollar symbol (e.g. A$ or yourname$.)

Constants

These are predefined values that do not change as the program is executed. Constants are either literal or symbolic. There are two kinds of literal constants: numeric and string. Numeric constant is any positive or negative number. A string constant is any sequence of characters enclosed by a double quotation mark (e.g. "CHEM 151" or " The class size is limited to 40 students."). A symbolic constant is used in place of numeric or string values. It follows the same rule for use of variables. A constant type may be indicated by the inclusion of type declaration character. The use of these characters is shown in Table 9.1

Table 9.1 BASIC declaration symbols

Symbol (suffix)	Purpose	Example
%	Integer values	sum%
&	long-integer values	sum&
#	Double-precision	sum#
!	Single-precision	sum!
$	String- Variable	sum$

EXPRESSIONS AND OPERATORS

Using computers for calculation or manipulation of strings involve the use of formula that must be expressed in a particular manner to the computer using expressions and operators. BASIC provides the programmer five kinds of operators. These are summarized below.

ARITHMETIC OPERATORS

These are used to perform calculations. The operations and the corresponding BASIC equivalents are given in Table 9.2

Table 9.2 Arithmetic operators

Operation symbols	BASIC representation
Exponentiation	^
Multiplication	*
Division	/
Addition	+
Subtraction	-

Table 9.2 has been arranged in the order in which arithmetic operations are performed. However, this order can be overruled by the use of parenthesis, since what is in the parenthesis is executed first. Using these operators formulas or expressions can be entered into the computer as demonstrated in Table 9.3.

Table 9.3 BASIC Representation of Algebraic Expression

Algebraic Expression Expression	BASIC Expression
x^4	x^4
xy/z	x*y/z
$\frac{x+y}{z}$	(x + y)/z
$(xy)^{2z}$	(x*y)^(2*z)

RELATIONAL OPERATORS

When it is desired to compare either strings or numeric values or to make decision regarding the flow of the program, relational operators are used. The most frequently used relational operators and their functions are shown in Table 9.4

Table 9.4 Relational Operators and Their Functions

Operator	Relation tested	Expression
$=$	Equality	$x = y$
$<$	Less than	$x < y$
$>$	Greater than	$x > y$
$\leq$	Less than or equal to	$x <= y$
$\geq$	Greater than or equal to	$x >= y$
$\neq$	Inequality (Not equal to)	$x <> y$

LOGICAL OPERATORS

Logical operators are used to carry out tests on two or more relations. The result of the test is either true (non zero) or false (zero). The most frequently used logical operators are AND, NOT, and OR.

FUNCTIONAL OPERATORS

Functional operators are used to access predefined functions that are resident in the Q-Basic Library of functions. Some of these functional operators are shown in Table 9.5.

Table 9.5 Mathematical Functions and BASIC Expressions

Math Function	BASIC Expression
$\sqrt{x}$	SQR(x)
Sin x	SIN(x)
Cos x	COS(x)
Tan x	TAN(x)
$\text{Tan}^{-1} x$	ATN(x)
ln x	LOG(x)
e^x	EXP(x)
$|x|$	ABS(x)

STRING OPERATORS

A string is a sequence of characters (alphabetic or numeric) or symbols. Strings are used for processing of nonnumerical data. In BASIC, any variable name followed by the dollar sign is a string (e.g. A$ or U$).

String operators are useful in comparing strings. As illustration of its usage, suppose that you want your program to continue only if it is used by you and your name is John Doe and you have defined a string variable Name$. When your program runs it checks to see if the name entered through the key board is the same as John Doe that is it checks if Name$="John Doe". Note that the name is put in double quotation mark.

INPUT AND OUTPUT STATEMENTS

In using the computer, the first concern is how the computer can be instructed to accept a given set of data and how to make it "spill out" the results obtained. Therefore, our first concern is with the input of data. There are two ways to input data into the computer using BASIC. The first is by the **INPUT** command and the second is through the use of the **READ** command. The format for both are given below.

INPUT Statement Format
   The format is

        INPUT [;]["promptstring" {; ,}] variable list

Each part of the format has meaning. The use of the symbol [] means that every thing inside is optional. The first semicolon following INPUT keeps the cursor on the same line after the enter button is pressed. The prompt string is a string of constant or variable printed before any prompt (i.e ?) appears when the program is run. The second semi-colon assures that a question mark is printed after the prompt where as the comma suppresses its printing. The variable list is a list of variables that are to be accepted by the computer and they must be separated by commas. Examples are given below:

     INPUT;"Enter your name, two numbers x and y";Name$,x,y
       or
     INPUT Name$, x,y

READ Statement Format

The **READ** statement is always followed by a **DATA** statement, therefore, both are presented together. Note that the

DATA statement can be placed anywhere on the program and any number of DATA statement necessary to enter all the data may be used.

The format then is
    READ variable list

    .

    .

    DATA constant1, [constant2]

Examples

    READ Name$,x,y
    DATA "John Doe",3.45,0.0004
or
    READ Name$,x,y
    DATA "John Doe"
    DATA 3.45,0.0004

OUTPUT STATEMENT FORMAT

There are two output statements often used in BASIC to output data to the screen. They are the **PRINT** and **WRITE** commands. Their formats are given below.

    PRINT [expressionlist][{, ;}]
    WRITE [expressionlist]

The expressionlist can be a string or a constant. The variables in the expressionlist are to be separated by a comma. The effect is different for the two statements. In the **PRINT** statement, the comma causes the result to be printed in defined fields which are 14 spaces apart. But the results are separated by commas in the case of the **WRITE** command. The comma or semicolon at the end of the expression list causes the next PRINT statement to print on the same line. Another difference between the two formats is in the output of string variables. The PRINT statement causes the string variable to be printed without a double quotation mark where as the WRITE statement outputs a string by enclosing it in double quotation mark.

Examples

```
    PRINT"My name is";Name$,x,y
or
    PRINT Name$, x+y, x^y
    WRITE Name$,x,y
```

ASSIGNMENT STATEMENT

Assignment statement is used to give values to data during the execution of the program. The general format is

[**LET**]variable = expression

Example

```
    LET x = 3
    LET x = x + 2*x
or
        x = 3
        x = x + 2*x
```

Note that the equality sign used here means replace. The second statement is only telling the computer to replace the value of x with the three times the original value of x. Although it is preferable to have one statement on a line, it may save space if two or more expressions are put on a line, but they must be separated by a colon, for example the above could be written:

        x = 3 : x = x + 2*x

It is advisable that those learning how to program should **not** write two statements on the same line.

SELECTION CONSTRUCTS

In the process of using the computer to solve problems, there is always the need to make choices as to what course of action to take. The ability to make a choice is provided by the use of **IF...THEN. ELSE** construct. There are two forms: single line and block. The block format is useful for complex operations. The single-line format is

IF <condition> **THEN** <statement> [**ELSE** <statement>]

Example

IF x > y   THEN z = x-y ELSE z = y-x
IF A$="John Doe" THEN PRINT A$

The format for the block type is

```
IF < condition> THEN
   <statement(s)>
[ELSEIF <condition> THEN
   <statement(s)>]
[ELSE
   <statement(s)>]
END IF
```

Examples

(a) IF x > 10 THEN
        y = x+ x^3 + x^2 + 10
        value = y/10
     ELSEIF x = 10
        y = x^4 + 20
        value = 2*y
     ELSE
        value = 40
     END IF
(b) IF x < = -3 THEN
        sum = sum + (3*x)^3
        PRINT "The sum is";sum
     END IF

REPETITIVE CONSTRUCTS

When it becomes necessary to repeat a block of statements, the repetitive constructs are used. Two of the most commonly used constructs are; **FOR...NEXT** Loops and **DO...LOOP** Loops. The difference between the two is that the first requires the user to know the exact number of times the block statements are to be executed while the second requires a test to check if a prescribed stopping criteria has been satisfied for it to finish executing. Consequently, the second (**DO...LOOP**) is used for iteration where the exact iteration number is unknown. The format for the **FOR...NEXT** Loop is

    FOR counter = start **TO** end [**STEP** step size]
      [statement(s)]
    NEXT [counter [,counter]]

where "counter" is a numeric variable used as a counter for the loop, "start" is the initial value of the counter, "end" is the final value of the counter, and "step size" is the amount the counter is incremented each time. If the increment is to be unity (1) then it may be omitted.   Note it is permissible to have another **FOR...NEXT** Loop inside another so long as it is properly executed.

Examples

```
(a)    sum = 0
      FOR I = 1 TO 21  STEP 2
        sum = sum +  I
      NEXT I
(b)   FOR X = 1 TO 30
        sum = sum + 1
      NEXT

(c)  FOR X = 1 TO 30
       FOR Y = 1 TO 10
         sum = sum + X*Y : PRINT X,Y,sum
       NEXT Y : sum = 0
     NEXT X
```

The format for the **DO...LOOP** Loop is

    DO [{WHILE_UNTIL} condition]
      < statement(s)>
    LOOP
or
    DO
      <statement(s)>
    LOOP [{WHILE_UNTIL} condition]

Example

The example given below is used to solve for the root of the equation $xe^x - 3\cos(\pi x) = 0$. Run it at the computer.

```
test= 1: pi = 22/7 : x = .1
DO UNTIL test < = .01
    x = x + .01
    test = x*EXP(x) - 3*Cos(pi*x)
    test =ABS(test)
LOOP
PRINT "The solution is:";x
```

or

```
test= 1: pi = 22/7 : x = .1
DO
    x = x + .01
    test = x*EXP(x) - 3*Cos(pi*x)
    test =ABS(test)
LOOP UNTIL test <= .01
PRINT "The solution is:";x
```

SUBSCRIPT VARIABLES AND ARRAYS

Q-BASIC allows variables to be subscripted. It is possible to enter a series of variables such as A_1, A_2,...,A_n or even $A_{1,2}$ in the computer. The term Array is used to refer to a series of variables that are referenced by the same name and each member of the set is known as a subscripted variable. An array is declared in BASIC by the use of a dimension statement. The dimension statement is used to define the maximum number of elements in an array. The format for a dimensional statement is

DIM variable (number of elements)...

or

DIM variable (lower subscript to upper subscript)...

Examples

```
    DIM A(20)
    DIM A(20),X(100),Y(200)
    DIM TABLE(5,15), Z(10,5)
or
    DIM TABLE(0 TO 5, 0 TO 15), Z(0 TO 10, 0 TO 5)
```

It was pointed before that comments should be used to make your programming readable by others. In BASIC it can be done using the statement **REM** at the beginning of the line you want to be a comment or you can use the single quotation mark ('). Examples are:

REM   This program is for solving a system of linear equations.
or
  ' This statement is for solving a system of linear equations.

USER DEFINED FUNCTIONS

Table 9.5 contains the functions that are predefined in the Q-Basic Library. However, Q-Basic allows a user defined function.   There are at least two methods of defining functions in Q-Basic.   Only one of them is given here. For further information you should consult a Q-Basic book.   The format for the simple way of defining a function is:

DEF FNname [(*parameter list*)] = expression

The word "name" that is attached to FN can be any legal variable name up to 40 characters long, together with FN forms the name of the function. The *parameter list* is a list of variables separated by commas that define the function. The "expression" is the function to be evaluated. To obtain a value of the function it should be assigned to another variable. Example provided below helps to clarify the use of user defined function.

Example

Suppose it is needed to evaluate two functions: one of single variable $y = x^3 + 4x^2 - 8$ at $x = 1.508$ and the other of two variables, $z = x^2 + xy^3$ at (1.5,2.3). This can be achieved using **DEF FN** as follows:.

```
DEF FNY(X) = X^3 + 4*X^2 -8
DEF FNZ (X,Y) = X^2 +X*Y^3
         Y = FNY(1.508)
         Z = FNZ(1.5,2.3)
   PRINT "Z=";Z;"Y =";Y
```

LINE GRAPHICS IN BASIC

Q-Basic makes it easy to plot functions using line graphics. Basically three commands are required. These commands are **SCREEN**, **PSET** and **LINE**. The **SCREEN** commands selects the appropriate mode for a particular display. The PSET command is used to draw a point on the screen. The **LINE** command is for drawing a line on the screen. The formats of these commands are as follows:

```
LINE (x1,y1) - (x2,y2),[color] [,[B[F]]]
PSET (x,y)[,color]
SCREEN Mode [,colorburst]
```

The "B " in the line command produces a box while BF results in filed box. The term "Mode" defines the type of screen mode. For example, 0 switches the screen to text, while 1 and 2 switch the screen to medium and high resolution respectively. To use the color command you should consult a Q-Basic manual since it is limited by the type of screen resolution chosen. An example of graphing a function is given to demonstrate the use of the above commands.

Example

Let us graph the function with one variable defined in the last example

```
SCREEN 2
CLS :'   This is a command for clearing the screen
PSET (0,0)
DEF FNY(X) = X^3 + 4*X^2 - 8
FOR  X = 1   TO 3  STEP .25
        Y = FNY(X)
        LINE - (X,Y)
NEXT X
```

Note that the form "LINE -(X,Y)" means that the line begins from the previous point. It was made possible in this example because of the use of PSET command. Run this example.

PROGRAMMING EXAMPLE

Consider the problem of determining the diameter of a piston rod used in hydraulic cylinders. The problem is to write a program that allows an engineer to determine the appropriate diameter of the rod for a specified load.

Step 1

The first step is to find the appropriate equation. There are two such equations:

Johnson's Formula (modified for round column)

$$P_{cr} = \frac{\pi d^2 S_y}{4}\left[1 - \frac{4C}{d^2}\right] \text{ if } \frac{16C}{d^2} \leq 2$$

Euler's Formula (modified for round column)

$$P_{cr} = \frac{\pi S_y d^4}{64C} \quad \text{if } \frac{16C}{d^2} > 2$$

where,
   P_{cr} = critical load
   S_y = yield strength
   d   = diameter
and

$$C = \frac{S_y L^2}{2\pi^2 E}$$

where,

    L = length of column

    E = modulus of elasticity.

The critical load is related to the actual load as follows:

    $P_{cr} = nP$

where,

    n = factor of safety

    P = applied load

Step 2

The second step involves the analysis of the problem. The objective of the program is to output diameter. The input and output are:

    Input: L, n, S_y, E, P

    Output : d

Since the output is diameter, the formulas must be solved for d:

$$d = \sqrt{\frac{4}{\pi S_y}\left(P_{cr} + \pi S_y C\right)} \quad \text{if } \frac{16C}{d^2} \leq 2 \text{, otherwise}$$

$$d = \sqrt[4]{\frac{64 P_{cr} C}{\pi S_y}}$$

Step 3

The next step is algorithm design. A flow chart is constructed (see Figure 9.5).

Step 4

The next step is to code or write the program using the flow chart. The resultant program is given in Figure 9.6.

Step 5

The final step is verification of the problem. Run the program and verify the solution (by hand calculation)using the following information:

        Length = 1.2 m

        Load   = 178 kN

        S_y = 41 MPa

        E   = 207 Gpa and n = 2.

163

```
*********************************
' This program calculates the piston*
' rod diameter to prevent buckling  *
'*********************************
INPUT "Length of rod"; l
INPUT "Load"; p
INPUT "Modulus of elasticity"; e
INPUT "Yield strength"; sy
INPUT "Factor of safety"; n
'----------------------------------
'Note that the input statements could
'have been combined in one line using
' Input, l,p,e,sy,n.  But it is better
'to let the user know what is being
'input
'----------------------------------
'Define constant pi
 pi = 22 / 7
'Calculate C
    c = sy * l ^ 2 / (2 * pi ^ 2 * e)
'----------------------------------
'Calculate Pcr
   pcr = n * p
'Calculate d using Johnson's formula
' Break the equation into smaller parts
x1 = 4 / (pi * sy)
x2 = pcr + pi * sy * c
d = (x1 * x2) ^ .5
' Compute test
 test = 16 * c / d ^ 2
 IF test > 2 THEN
    d = (64 * pcr * c / (pi * sy)) ^ (1 / 4)
END IF
PRINT "The diameter is:"; d
```

Figure 9.6 Program listing for the column example

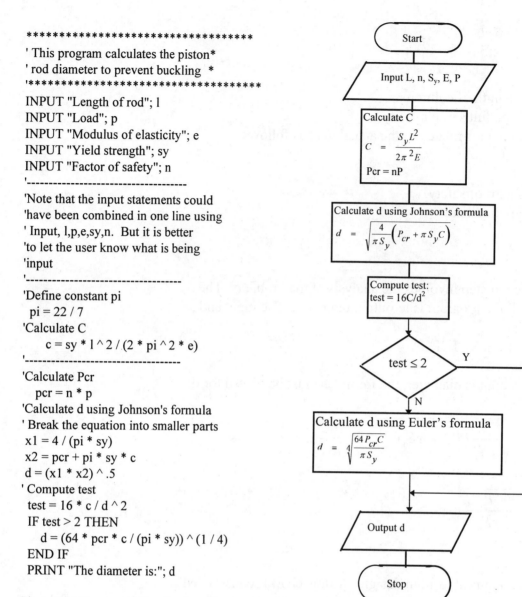

Figure 9.5 Flowchart for the column example

9.6 COMPUTER APPLICATION PACKAGES

An engineering student must be aware of the many available software packages. Some of these you need to learn how to use. However, it is important that you do not become consumed with their use to the point that you forget to learn the principles behind them. The method of software development has been introduced. The engineer must be capable of developing his or her own little application software. However, many introduced. The engineer must be capable of developing his or her own little application software. However, many application software packages are commercially available. You must become familiar with at least one **word processor**, **spreadsheet** and an **equation solver** such as **MathCad** or similar type software. A brief description of each of these software packages is given below.

WORD PROCESSORS

The most widely used application software packages are word processors. Word processors are software packages that makes it easy to communicate information. It is similar to the use of typewriters. However, the text typed are directly stored by the computer and this makes it easy to edit or even change the appearance of the text.

Word processors have become sophisticated in that most of them allow the user to include graphics within the text. Also, complex equations can easily be included in the text by using the particular equation editor of the software package. Another important feature of word processors is that they include dictionaries to check your spelling when you finish your document. Of course it is not automatic, you must still tell the particular word processor to do it for you. Also, you may use the Thesaurus included to select alternative words to make your written communication interesting to the reader. There are many attractive features of the word processors such as formatting your text, ability to change line spacing easily within the same text, copying a paragraph from one place to another. It is therefore, your responsibility to understand some of the features of your chosen word processor. Remember that there is really one way of becoming proficient with any software, that is using it.

SPREADSHEETS

Spreadsheets are computer programs that are used to enter data, perform calculations and prepare certain kinds of reports. They are extremely useful in evaluating alternative course of actions that involve numerical computations. In other words, when a "what if" situation exists spreadsheets are most useful. There are many spreadsheet programs available. Some of these are **LOTUS 1-2-3, QUATTRO PRO** and **EXCEL**.

A typical spreadsheet consists of a rectangular grid of columns and rows (see Figure 9.7). Each column is referenced by a letter that normally ranges from A to Z and the rows are intersection second column and fourth row. The area that data is entered then is known as the **worksheet**.

Spreadsheets make it easy to enter formulas by using one or more cell locations. Typical formula entry is shown in Table 9.6. Function statements are also used to perform some defined operations. Typical function commands are shown in Table 9.7 and the format of these commands are shown in Table 9.8

166

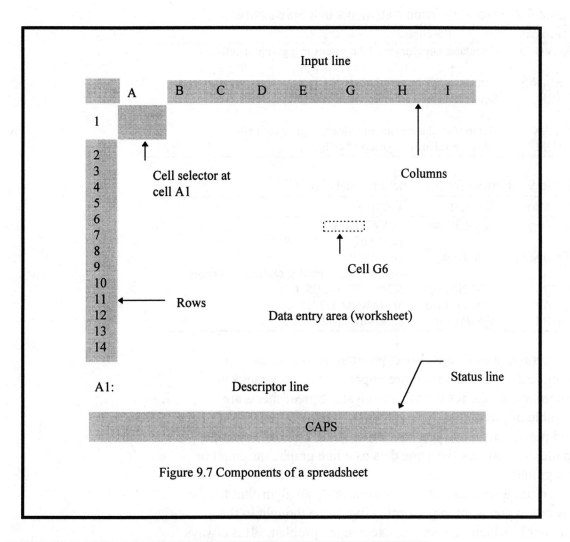

Figure 9.7 Components of a spreadsheet

Table 9.6 Typical formula entry in a Spreadsheet	
Formula Entered	Meaning
+ A3+A4+A8	Add the values in cells A3,A4, and A8
+E4+G3-D5	Add the value in cell E4 to the value in G3 then subtract the value in cell D5 from its result
+H4/F6	Divide the value in cell H4 by the value in cell F6
+C5*P3-B4	Multiple the value in cell C5 by the value in cell P3 and from the result subtract the value in cell B4.
+U15^2	Square the value in cell U15.

Table 9.7 Typical function statements in a Spreadsheet

Statement	Function
@AVG	Calculates the average of the values in a group of cells
@ASIN(X)	Calculates the arc sin of angle X
@MIN	Determines the minimum value in a group of cells
@MAX	Determines the maximum value in a group of cells
@SUM	Adds the values in a group of cells

Table 9.8 Format for the functions in Table 9.7

Function	Format	Example
@AVG	@AVG(List)	@AVG(B2..G2)
		@AVG(B2..B9,E3..E9)
@ASIN(X)	@ASIN(X)	@ASIN(0.8)
		Note value returned in radians not degrees
@MIN	@MIN(List)	@MIN(B2..G2,B5..E5)
@MAX	@MAX(List)	@MAX(B2..G2,B5..E5)
@SUM	@SUM(List)	@SUM(B2..G2,B5..E5)

Another use of spreadsheet program is to present data graphically. It is always more impressive to use graphs to communicate the results of an analysis. Spreadsheets are capable of presenting different types of graphs such as line, bar and pie. In fact, once you have entered the data, it is a simple matter to represent the same data as a line graph, bar graph or pie graph.

To use a spreadsheet you must develop an algorithm for the operation you want to perform. Give some thought to the manner in which you want to execute the problem. It is always useful to write out your algorithm before you sit down to use a spreadsheet.

Example of an algorithm for spreadsheet

Consider the equation that allows one to determine the amount of twist in a solid shaft . This equation is given below:

$$\theta = \frac{TL}{JG}$$

$$J = \frac{\pi d^4}{32}$$

where,

θ = angle of twist

T = torque

d = diameter of shaft

G = modulus of rigidity

Suppose T = 2200 N · m, G = 80 GPa, L = 400 mm, and d = 30 mm. Then, the algorithm may be written as follows:

Cell location	Enter
A1	Torque
A2	Length
A3	Modulus,G
A4	diameter
A5	Pi
A6	Theta
B1	2200
B2	0.40
B3	80E9
B4	0.030
B5	= 22/7
C1	= B5*B4^4/32
C6	= B1*B2/(C1*B3)

Now try it in the spreadsheet in your computer. Note that the last two entries could also be replaced by one entry such as

B6   = B1*B2/((B5*B4^4/32)*B3)

EQUATION SOLVERS

Equation solvers are engineering tools that allow you to solve different kinds of problems without having to use the conventional programming languages. Some of these are **TK solver Plus**, **Mathcad**, and **Matlab**.

Some of the solvers combine the capabilities of spreadsheets and programming languages in a way that it is easy to use. In case of MathCad, for example, you enter the formula as you encounter them without having to put them in the form required by a spreadsheet. Mathcad, similar to Matlab, allows you to do graphing both in two dimension and three dimension. It also allows you the option of adding text to your document. In short with such a tool you can do almost any thing you need for engineering analysis in the areas of electrical, civil, and mechanical engineering.

SOURCES USED

Dodd, G.G. "Elements of Data management Systems", **Computer Survey 1,2** June 1969, pp 115 - 135.

Ellzey, Roy, **Data Structures For Computer Information Systems,** Science Research Associates, Chicago, 1982.

Kassab, V., **Technical C Programming**, Prentice-Hall Englewood Cliffs, New Jersey, 1989.

Bradley, J.C., **Quick BASIC- Using Modular Structure**, Wm.C. Brown Publishers, Dubuque, Iowa, 1988.

Linger, R.C., Mills, H.D., Witt, B.I., **Structured Programming Theory and Practice**, Addison - Wesley Publishing Company, Reading, Massachusetts, 1979.

Marca, David, Applying **Software Engineering Principles**, Little, Brown and Company, Boston, 1984.

Myers, G.J., **Composite/Structure Design**, Van Nostrand Reinhold Company, New York, 1978.

Tassel, D.V., **Program Style, Design, Efficiency, Debugging and Testing,** Prentice - Hall, Englewood Cliffs, New Jersey, 1978.

Onwubiko, C., **Foundations of Computer Aided Design**, West Publishing Company, St. Paul, Minnesota, 1989.

Yaohan, Chu, **Software Blueprint and Examples**, Books, D.C. Heath and Company, Lexington, Massachusetts, 1982. Microsoft QuickBASIC 4.0, Basic Language Reference, Microsoft, 1987.

PROBLEMS

9.1 What is firmware?

9.2 Define software and give seven characteristics of good software.

9.3 Give the steps involved in the design of software.

9.4 What does the term "good programming environment" mean?

9.5 Write a program that accepts your name only and then finds the average of four numbers. Verify your program by using the name John Doe and the numbers 4588.68, 3568.5, 1389, and -3210.5.

9.6 Write a program that will sum all the odd numbers between 1 and 1000 and prints out their average.

9.7 Write a program that reads the matrix **A** and prints it out in rows.

$$A = \begin{bmatrix} 1 & -3 & 2 & 8 \\ 5 & 0 & 6 & 12 \\ -2 & 7 & 4 & 10 \\ 3 & 4 & 3 & -2 \end{bmatrix}$$

9.8 Write a program that will evaluate the equation
$$y = x^3 + (128-x^2)^{\frac{1}{2}}$$
from x =0 to 12. (Hint: pay attention to fact that the square root of a negative number can not be taken.)

9.9 The derivative of a function at any point may be obtained
using $f' = \dfrac{f(x+h) - f(x)}{h}$
where h is a small increment. Using h = 0.01, develop a program that can evaluate the derivative of a given function. Verify your program by finding the derivatives at the point x = .5 of the following:

(a)Sinx

(b)tanx

(c)$3e^{3x} - 6x^3$.

What is the error in each derivative computed?

9.10 Solve the equation $e^x - 3x^2 = 0$. Start at the point x = 0.4, use a tolerance of 0.0001. How many iterations were involved?

9.11 Use the computer to graph the following

(a) $y = e^x - 3x^2$ $(0 \le x \le 3)$.

(b) $y = x^3 + 6x^2 - 3x + 2$ $(0 \le x \le 2)$

(c) $y = \cos x$ $(-\pi \le x \le \pi)$

9.12 The Q-Basic library does not normally include arcsine. Write a program to compute the arcsine of a given value of x. It may be approximated using

$$\sin^{-1} x = x + \frac{1}{2}\left(\frac{x^3}{3}\right) + \left(\frac{1 \times 3}{2 \times 4}\right)\left(\frac{x^5}{5}\right) + \left(\frac{1 \times 3 \times 5}{2 \times 4 \times 6}\right)\left(\frac{x^7}{7}\right) + \cdots$$

Verify your solution by finding arcsine of 0.5. What is the error?

9.13 Use a spreadsheet to determine the average of the data shown in Table 9.10. If the value of data #2 is changed to 20.05, and that of data #3 is now 21.5, what is the new average.?

Table 9.10. Data for problem 9.12

Data #	Value
1	23.60
2	10.85
3	41.75
4	30.65
5	17.25
6	14.00
7	21.70

9.14 The diameter of a short column may be determined using:

$$d = \sqrt{\frac{4}{\pi S_y}\left(P_{cr} + \pi S_y C\right)}$$

where,

$$C = \frac{S_y L^2}{2\pi^2 E}$$

S_y = yield stress
L = length
E = modulus of elasticity
P_{cr} = critical load.

Several materials are to be considered (see Table 9.11) for design. Specify the material number and the diameter that results in a column of smallest mass for a critical load of 350 kN. The length of the column is 1.219 m. Use a spreadsheet to solve this problem.

Table 9.11. Materials for problem 9.13

Material Identification number	S_y (MPa)	Density (kg/m³)	E (GPa)
1	207	7 680	207
2	165	2 820	70
3	290	2 730	70
4	290	7 680	207
5	490	7 680	207
6	627	2 790	70

9.15 The stress due to bending on a beam is obtained using:

$$\sigma = \frac{Mc}{I}$$

where , $I = \frac{1}{12}bh^3$

   b = width (m)

   h = height (m)

   c = h/2 (m)

   M = moment (N·m)

   σ = stress (Pa).

A beam is subjected to a bending moment of 4 750 N·m.
Consider the data given in Table 9.12 and answer the following:

(a) What is the minimum stress on the beam?

(b) Which cross-sectional area gives the maximum bending stress?

(c) If the permissible bending stress is 7 MPa, which cross section will you recommend?

Table 9.12 Data for problem 9.15

Cross-section number	width (mm)	height (mm)
1	100	250
2	158	158
3	250	100
4	150	175
5	120	180
6	161	161

NOTES

CHAPTER 10

HANDLING DATA - STATISTICS

10.1 INTRODUCTION

Engineers make series of decisions in their every day design activities. It is well known that good decisions are based on good information. To the engineer this information is generally in the form of data. Data can be a result of a survey of people's opinions or results of an experiment conducted in a research laboratory. The way data is obtained affects its usefulness. The idea of data brings into question at least two questions: how is the data obtained and what can we do with it? These two questions are addressed in a branch of study called **statistics**. *Statistics may be defined as both an art and a science that deals with gathering, analyzing and interpreting numerical data.*

An engineer Analyzing results of a computer output to help make design decision.

Statistics are utilized in many ways by different engineers. An engineer may be uncertain about the ability of a material to withstand a given load and so a series of tests may be necessary to determine the load carrying ability of the material in question. To carry out of this experiment and to analyze the result involves the use of statistics. A traffic engineer contemplating the installation of signal light at an intersection may use statistical data collected at different time periods to determine the average traffic flow at the intersection and with this information can make a decision as to whether or not a signal light should be installed. In a manufacturing plant the quality of manufactured goods is controlled by use of statistics. The quality control engineer periodically counts the number of defects in a production line to determine whether the production line is functioning at an acceptable level.

While it is true that some big companies such as General Motors or General Electric have a group of statisticians who delve into the complexities of statistics, each engineer must have some working knowledge of this field. As an engineering student you will make use of this field during your laboratory courses, therefore, in this chapter the essential features of statistics with which the engineer should be familiar are introduced.

10.2 FREQUENCY DISTRIBUTION

Often data may be collected and recorded in such a way that it is difficult to understand. Consider the data obtained by an instructor about the weight of the students in a class, presented in the form shown in Table 10.1

Table 10.1 Students weight (lbs)

145	165	203	187	198	123	117	156
143	163	193	117	178	185	203	147
123	124	207	156	148	159	158	152
207	133	138	136	182	175	152	173

The data may better be handled if it is grouped into class intervals and the frequency of occurrence of data in each group noted. The grouping is shown in Table 10.2.

Table 10.2 Grouping of data of Table 10.1

Weight (lbs)	Tally	Frequency
111 - 120	| |	2
121 - 130	| | |	3
131 - 140	| | |	3
141 - 150	| | | |	4
151 - 160	| | | | | |	6
161 - 170	| |	2
171 - 180	| | |	3
181 - 190	| |	3
191 - 200	| |	2
201 - 210	| | | |	4

The data shown in Table 10.2 can be represented graphically. If the class interval is represented in the horizontal axis and the frequency is represented in the vertical axis, the resulting graph is known as **histogram** (see Figure 10.1). The histogram ,being a type of graphical representation, actually represents the frequency distribution of the number of occurrences in each class interval. It is clear that Figure 10.1 is easier to comprehend and interpret than the data in Table 10.1.

Certain factors involved in constructing a histogram should be noted. First, note that the class interval is chosen so that each data falls into only one class. Second, the range selected covered the entire set of data. Third, equal intervals were used in the above case. Although this is preferred, unequal class interval may also be used. Finally, the class boundary is chosen in such a way that none of the numbers fall on the boundary of

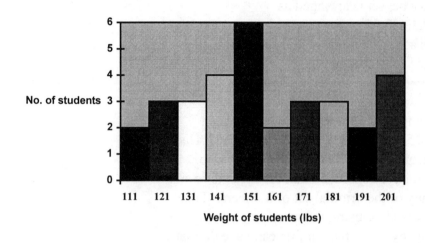

Weight of students (lbs)

Figure 10.1 Histogram for the data in Table 10.1

the class.

10.3 MEASURE OF CENTRAL TENDENCY

In statistics a major concern is the ability to use the information from a sample to draw conclusions with regard to the population from which the data was drawn. Consequently, it is desirable to describe the data by one or two numbers that uniquely characterize the set of data. One measure used to do this has to do with the center of the data or its **average**. This measure which characterizes the center is generally known as measure of central tendency. The most popular measure of the central tendency is the arithmetic mean and it is defined as

$$\bar{x} = \frac{1}{n}\sum_{i=1}^{n} x_i \qquad (10.1)$$

The other measures of central tendency are the **median** and the **mode**. The median is the middle term of a set of data arranged either in an ascending or descending order. The mode is the most frequently occurring number in a set of data.

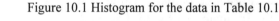

Example 10.1
Determine the mean, median and the mode of the following set of numbers: 34, 45, 36, 50,55,48,36,44,53.

Solution

Using (10.1) the mean $= 401/9 = 44.556$
To obtain the median the set is arranged as
 34,36,36,44,45,48,50,53,55
hence the median is 45. The mode is 36 because it is the
number that appeared most frequently.

Suppose that in Example 10.1 the last number has been
incorrectly entered as 155, the mean then becomes 55.67. Had
that been a result from an experimental result the one who
analyzed the data could have concluded that the mean is 55.67.
which is higher than any of the original set of numbers. This
observation is one drawback to using the mean as a measure of
central tendency since any error in a number can have dramatic
effect on the mean. The standard practice is that if value of the
mean is highly influenced by the inclusion of the highest and
lowest values in a set, then the median is used as a measure of
central tendency.

10.4 MEASURE OF VARIATIONS

In the last section a measure of centrality of the data as a
method of describing a set of data was examined.   Another
measure for characterizing data is the measure of variation. The
mean, for example, does not reveal how close or how scattered a
given set of data is. For example the set {3,4,5} has a mean of
4 so does the set {1,2,3,10} and yet the difference between the
smallest and the largest number in both sets are not the same.
Therefore, in dealing with a given set of data it is useful to
provide a measure of variation in the data set. This measure
allows us to indicate how the data are dispersed (scattered) or
clustered together.   There are several parameters used to
measure variation of data. The two most often used are the
range and the **standard deviation**.   The range is simply the
difference between the largest number and the smallest number
in the set. For example, in the first set given above, the range is
2 while for the second set the range is 9.
The standard deviation is the most commonly used statistics
to measure the scatter in a given set of data. It is a composite
sum of the squares of the individual deviations from the mean
of the given data. The standard deviation, s, for a given sample
(a group of objects that statistical information is needed) is
computed using

$$s = \sqrt{\frac{\sum_{i=1}^{n}(x_i - \bar{x})^2}{n - 1}} \qquad (10.2)$$

Using the definition in (10.1) a more convenient form of (10.2) is

$$s = \sqrt{\frac{n\sum_{i=1}^{n}x_i^2 - \left(\sum_{i=1}^{n}x_i\right)^2}{n(n - 1)}} \qquad (10.3)$$

Often the term **variance** is encountered which is the square of the sample standard deviation (i.e. s^2).

The student should not confuse the standard deviation for a sample from the standard deviation of the population (entire group that forms the object of statistical study). The standard deviation, σ, for a population is computed using

$$\sigma = \sqrt{\frac{\sum_{i=1}^{n}(x_i - \mu)^2}{n}} \qquad (10.4)$$

where,

μ = population mean
n = no of data points
x_i = value of data.

Example 10.2

The test scores in a class are shown in Table 10.3. What is the range, the standard deviation, and the variance?

Table 10.3 Test scores for a class

95	81	63	84	91	70	88	97
70	76	80	77	78	91	93	60
85	79	84	90				

Solution

The highest score is 97 and the lowest score is 60,

therefore, the range is 37.

Using (10.3), with n = 20

$$s = [(135\ 186\ -(1632)^2)/(20)(19)]^{0.5} = 10.2977$$
The variance is $s^2 = 106.0426$

10.5 PROBABILITY AND NORMAL DISTRIBUTION

The game of chance such as rolling a dice is a well known concept. Chance as a concept introduces the idea of uncertainty. Engineers are always faced with uncertainties regarding their design. For example, a structural engineer designs a structure which he believes will withstand an earthquake of certain magnitude, but no one is ever sure of the likelihood that an earthquake of that magnitude will ever be encountered or even exceeded. It is because of such a potential incident that engineers deal with probability.

Probability in its simplest definition is a numerical measure of the likelihood of occurrence of an event. In tossing of a fair coin there are two possible outcomes: a head or a tail, therefore the probability of the outcome being a head or a tail is 1/2. If it is certain that an event will take place then the probability is 1. On the other hand, if an event is impossible then the probability is zero. For example, the probability that when a coin is tossed that neither head nor tail will show up is zero. An important question is how can probabilities be determined? The simplest answer is by conducting an experiment. At this point the probability of an event must be viewed as the ratio of the number of outcomes (frequency) of that event to the total number of outcomes of the experiment. The determination of probability becomes simple, if the outcomes of the experiment are represented by either a graph or an equation. This graph or equation is generally known as **probability distribution model**. However, the mathematical representation is more commonly known as probability distribution function. The histogram is an example of probability distribution of discrete random variables. Note that a **random variable** is a variable whose values are determined by the outcome of an experiment.

One of the most popular type of distributions is the **normal distribution**. It is characterized by two parameters: the population mean, μ, and the population standard deviation, σ. Its graphical representation, which is bell-shaped and symmetrical about the mean, is shown in Figure 10.2. The mathematical representation of the distribution is

$$f(x) = \frac{1}{\sigma\sqrt{2\pi}}\, e^{-(x-\mu)^2/2\sigma^2} \qquad (10.5)$$

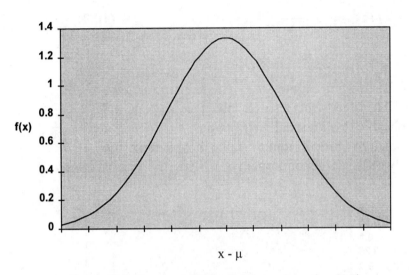

x - μ

Figure 10.2 A normal distribution curve (equation 10.5)

The area under the curve of Figure 10.2 is 1, that is

$$\int_{-\infty}^{\infty} \frac{1}{\sigma\sqrt{2\pi}}\, e^{-(x-\mu)^2/2\sigma^2}\, dx = 1 \qquad (10.6)$$

If the mean and standard deviation are known then, (10.6) can be used to determine the area of the curve between two points on the x-axis. For example, the area between two points x_1 and x_2 is

$$Area = \int_{x_1}^{x_2} \frac{1}{\sigma\sqrt{2\pi}}\, e^{-(x-\mu)^2/2\sigma^2}\, dx \qquad (10.7)$$

The evaluation of either (10.6) or (10.7) is not easy and so no tabulation exists for them. Furthermore, if we are to construct tables for them several tables have to be constructed for all conceivable mean and standard deviation. This is an impossible task. For this reason, the standard approach is to transform x into another variable, z, using

$$z = \frac{x - \mu}{\sigma} \tag{10.8}$$

If we assume $\mu = 0$ and $\sigma = 1$ then from (10.5)

$$f(z) = \frac{1}{\sqrt{2\pi}} e^{-0.5z^2} \tag{10.9}$$

and its graph is shown in Figure 10.3. This transformation makes it possible to construct a single table (see Appendix E) which is applicable to all normal distributions.

It is important to observe from the table in Appendix that approximately 68% of a set of normally

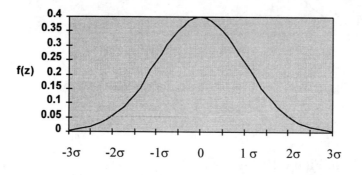

Figure 10.3   Standardized normal distribution curve (eq. 10.9)

distributed data points lie within ± 1 standard deviation from the mean. In other words about 68% of the area of Figure 10.3 lies in that range. Likewise, 95.4% of such data set lies ± 2 standard deviations from the mean and 99.7% of a normally distributed set of data lies within ±3 standard deviations from the mean.

Example 10.3
    A random variable has a mean of 25 and a standard deviation of 5. Assume that the variable has a normal distribution.
(a)What is the probability that the variable has a value less than 15?
(b)Determine the probability that the variable has a value between 15 and 40.

Solution

In each case eq.(10.8) is applied.
(a) $z = (15 - 25)/5 = -2$.   The negative sign simply means
that the variable is 2 standard deviations below the mean.
From Appendix E, the area between the mean and $z = -2$ is
0.4772. Therefore the probability that the variable is less
than 5 is $0.5 - 0.4772 = 0.0228$ (see Figure 10.4)
(b) $z = (40 - 25)/5 = 3$. From Appendix E, the area between
    $z = 0$ and $z = 3$ is 0.4987.   The probability of the
    variable having a value between 15 and $40 = 0.4772 +$
    $0.4987 = 0.9759$

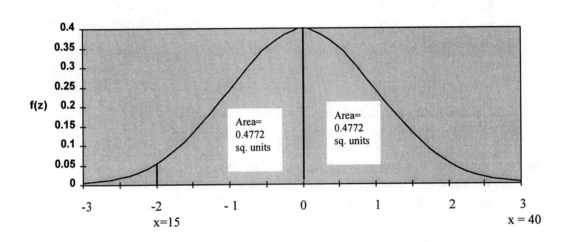

Figure 10. 4 Illustration of probability calculation of Example 10.3

10.6 LINEAR REGRESSION

Engineers like to work with mathematical models
(equations) when dealing with the relationship between
variables. This is particular useful in experimental work when
it is desired to study cause and effect. For example, Hook's
Law was discovered by studying the relationship between
applied load and the deformation caused by the load. When
data is obtained such as shown in Table 10.4 it is desirable to
know the relationship between them. One reason is that it may
be desirable to determine the value of y when $x = 1.75$ which is
not given in the original data.   If an equation exists that
describes the relationship between x and y, it becomes a matter
of using it to compute y for the given x value. Of course, if a

graph that is of x versus y exists, the desired value of y may also be determined. One method of finding a mathematical relationship between variables is often referred to as **regression analysis**. If there are two variables and the relationship between them can be modeled as a straight line then the regression is known as **linear regression**.

Consider the data of Table 10.4 shown in Figure 10.5. The question is how can we draw the straight line that best fits the data. Alternatively, we may seek an equation of the form

$$y = ax + b \qquad (10.10)$$

Table 10.4. Data resulting from a series of measurements

x	y	x	y
0.50	0.34	3.50	5.38
1.00	1.18	4.00	6.22
1.50	2.02	4.50	7.06
2.00	2.86	5.00	7.90
2.50	3.70	5.50	8.74
3.00	4.50		

Figure 10.5 Plot of data of Table 10.4

that best fits the data. The best values of a and b in (10.10) are determined by the **method of least square**. This involves minimizing the sum, S, of the squares of the difference between the actual value of y and that predicted by (10.10), that is to minimize

$$S = \sum_{i=1}^{n} \left[y_i - \left(ax_i + b \right) \right]^2 \qquad (10.11)$$

To determine the value of a and b that makes S minimum, we simply differentiate S with respect to a and b respectively and set the results to zero. This yields:

$$nb + a\sum_{i=1}^{n} x_i = \sum_{i=1}^{n} y_i \qquad (10.12)$$

$$b\sum_{i=1}^{n} x_i + a\sum_{i=1}^{n} x_i^2 = \sum_{i=1}^{n} x_i y_i \qquad (10.13)$$

Solving equations (10.12) and (10.13) gives

$$a = \frac{n\sum_{i=1}^{n} x_i y_i - \left(\sum_{i=1}^{n} x_i\right)\left(\sum_{i=1}^{n} y_i\right)}{n\sum_{i=1}^{n} x_i^2 - \left(\sum_{i=1}^{n} x_i\right)^2} \qquad (10.14)$$

$$b = \frac{\left(\sum_{i=1}^{n} x_i^2\right)\left(\sum_{i=1}^{n} y_i\right) - \left(\sum_{i=1}^{n} x_i\right)\left(\sum_{i=1}^{n} x_i y_i\right)}{n\sum_{i=1}^{n} x_i^2 - \left(\sum_{i=1}^{n} x_i\right)^2} \qquad (10.15)$$

Example 10.4

Find the equation of the line that fits the data in Table 10.4.

Solution

To apply equations (10.14) and (10.15) we set up the Table 10.5. From Table 10.5 and equations (10.14) and (10.15) we have

$$a = \frac{(11)(195.90) - (33)(49.90)}{(11)(126.5) - 33^2} = 1.68$$

and

$$b = \frac{(126.5)(49.90) - (33)(195.90)}{(11)(126.5) - 33^2} = -0.50$$

The equation then is of the form y = 1.68x - 0.50.

Table 10.5: Set up for example 10.4

i	x_i	x_i^2	y_i	$x_i y_i$
1	0.50	0.25	0.34	0.17
2	1.00	1.00	1.18	1.18
3	1.50	2.25	2.02	3.03
4	2.00	4.00	2.86	5.72
5	2.50	6.25	3.70	9.25
6	3.00	9.00	4.50	13.50
7	3.50	12.25	5.38	18.83
8	4.00	16.00	6.22	24.88
9	4.50	20.25	7.06	31.77
10	5.00	25.00	7.90	39.50
11	5.50	30.25	8.74	48.07
Σ	33.00	126.5	49.90	195.90

184

Example 10.5

The relationship between x and y of data shown in Table 10.6 may be represented by the equation of the form:

$$y = be^{ax}$$

Using the method of least squares, find the equation of the line of best fit.

Table 10.6 Data for example 10.5

x	y
3	90
7	54
13	25
19	11
27	4
33	2
37	1.1

Solution

The relationship between x and y is given as

$$y = be^{ax}$$

Taking the natural log of both sides of the equation gives:

$$\ln y = ax + \ln b \qquad (a)$$

Equation (a) is in form of straight line for which y is ln y, a is the slope and b is the intercept. Note the following equivalents

$\Sigma y \equiv \Sigma \ln y$

$\Sigma y^2 \equiv \Sigma (\ln y)^2$

$\Sigma xy \equiv \Sigma (x \ln y)$.

Following the same procedure as in example 10.4 results in Table 10.7.

Table 10.7. Set up for example 10.5

x	y	ln y	x^2	$(\ln y)^2$	x ln y
3	90	4.4998	9	20.2482	13.4994
7	54	3.9890	49	15.9120	27.9229
13	25	3.2189	169	10.3612	41.8454
19	11	2.3979	361	5.7499	45.5600
27	4	1.3863	729	1.9218	37.4299
33	2	0.6931	1089	0.4805	22.8739
37	1.1	0.0953	1369	0.0084	3.5265
Σ 139		16.2803	3775	54.6827	192.6580

Applying equations (10. 14) and (10.15):

a = -0.129 : ln b = 4.882, b = 131.839

The equation of best fit is $y = 131.839e^{-0.129x}$

10.7 COEFFICIENT OF CORRELATION

In the previous section we present a method of finding the best linear fit for a given set of data. A logical question is: how good is such a fit? The answer to this is obtained by the use of coefficient of correlation. Coefficient of correlation is a measure of the degree of linear relationship between two variables. The coefficient of correlation, r, is computed as

$$r = \frac{n\sum_{i=1}^{n} x_i y_i - \sum_{i=1}^{n} x_i \sum_{i=1}^{n} y_i}{\sqrt{\left[n\sum_{i=1}^{n} x_i^2 - \left(\sum_{i=1}^{n} x_i\right)^2\right]\left[n\sum_{i=1}^{n} y_i^2 - \left(\sum_{i=1}^{n} y_i\right)^2\right]}}$$

(10.16)

The coefficient of correlation lies between -1 and +1. If r = -1 then we have a perfect negative fit while r = +1 is an indication of a positive perfect fit. When there is no correlation whatsoever between the two variables the coefficient of correlation is zero (r = 0).

Example 10.6   What is the coefficient of correlation for the data given in Table 10.5?

Solution Using the results of example 10.4 and equation (10.16)

$$r = \frac{(11)(195.90) - (33)(49.90)}{\sqrt{[(11)(126.50) - 33^2][(11)(303.982) - 49.90^2]}} = 0.99999$$

It is clear that r is approximately 1 which suggest a perfect positive fit between y and x.

SOURCES USED

Braverman ,J.D., **Fundamentals of Business Statistics**, Academic Press, New York, 1979.

Scheaffer, R.L. and McClave, J.T., **Statistics for Engineers**, Duxury Press, Boston, 1982.

PROBLEMS

10.1   The test scores in a class are given in random fashion as:

63 72 85 65 73 74 88 83 82 77 78 92 94 68 72

87 88 85 83 82 64 73 92 59 96 62 94 83 87 87

73 55 83 67 87 93 47 64 87 95

Find

(a) the percentage of students who failed the test (i.e <60)

(b) the percentage of students with A (i.e. ≥ 90)

(c) the percentage of students with a score of at least 80.

10.2 Find the mode and median of the scores given in problem 10.1.

10.3 Construct the histogram for problem 10.1.

10.4   Find the mean and standard deviation for problem 10.1.

10.5 Write a program to compute the mean and standard deviation.

Use the data in Table 10.8 to verify your program.

Table 10.8 Diameters of rods (mm)

45.15	44.82	44.83	44.75	45.07	43.92
43.96	45.12	44.93	44.05	43.82	45.10
44.82	44.76	44.89	45.20	43.71	44.91
44.39	43.90	44.75	44.92	45.02	43.75

10.6 The mean height in a class of 50 students is 1.68 m and the standard deviation is and the standard deviation is 130 mm. If the distribution of the heights is approximately normal, determine:

(a) The number of students not less than 1.72 m tall

(b) The number of students between 1.60 m and 1.72 m

(c) The number of students not shorter than 1.85 m.

(d) The height of the tallest person in the shortest 10% group of the class.

10.7 A quality control engineer measures at random 100 rods. The mean diameter is 45.8 mm and the standard deviation is 0.75 mm. How many of the rods meet the required specification of 45.7 ± 1 mm? Assume normal distribution.

10.8 A company manufactures 1000 rivets. It was determined that the mean diameter is 25.5 mm and the standard deviation 0.8 mm. The standard practice is to reject all parts that do not meet the specification of 25.2 ± 1 mm. If the cost of labor and material is $0.75/rivet, what loss is the company suffering? How much difference would it have become if the specification had been 25.2 ± 0.5 mm?

10.9 A family moves into a house with a solar heating system. They are provided with experimental data for the efficiency of the solar collector as shown in Table 10.9

(a) Find the best equation that describes the given data (Hint: Treat η as the dependent variable)

(b) If the temperature difference, ΔT, is $40^\circ K$ and the solar flux incident on the collector, I_c, is 350 W/m^2 what is the collector efficiency?

(c) Calculate and interpret the coefficient of correlation.

Table 10.9 Data for Problem 10.9

Efficiency (η) %	$100\Delta T/I_c$ (K m^2/W)
70	0.018
65	0.028
64	0.032
59	0.041
55	0.052
58	0.056
53	0.066
48	0.082
30	1.34

10.10 The data shown in Table 10.10 is obtained in a cooling experiment. It is known that the relation between y and t can be represented as

$$y = Ce^{at}$$

Using the method of least squares, find the equation of the line of best fit.

Table 10.10. Data for problem 10.10.

t	y
0.2	1.08
0.5	0.88
0.8	0.59
1.8	0.21
2.3	0.13
3.3	0.05
4.1	0.02

CHAPTER 11

DECISION TOOL - OPTIMIZATION

11.1 INTRODUCTION

In engineering practice many problems arise that require making the best possible decision. For example, a manufacturing manager may be required to allocate resources among several operations in order to increase the overall efficiency of a manufacturing process. Alternatively, the manager may be required to plan and schedule the various operations efficiently in an effort to reduce costs. Similarly, an engineer may be required to design new, more efficient, but less expensive systems or to improve the performance of an existing system such as chemical processing plant. Another possible requirement may be to design a structure of minimum weight.

It is also important for the designer to continuously improve the design solution in order to obtain what may be termed the best solution under the design conditions. This means that the designer must understand the difference between adequate and optimum design. **Adequate design** can be defined as the selection of sizes and/or material needed to satisfy the functional requirements of the design while keeping the costs and undesirable effects within tolerable limits. Adequate design is usually based on engineering information available in equations, graphs (in handbooks), and the experience of the designer. **Optimum design** is the best design among several alternatives that meets a specified objective. It is usually obtained by those who understand a branch of mathematics called optimization. The purpose of this chapter is to introduce the student to some concepts involved in this interesting decision making tool. In its simplest form, optimization may be defined as a mathematical process of obtaining the set of conditions required to produce the maximum or the minimum value of a specified objective.

11.2 FUNDAMENTAL DEFINITIONS

DESIGN VARIABLES

An engineering optimization model consists of decision variables or parameters whose numerical values are to be determined in order to achieve an optimum design. These decision variables or parameters are called **design variables**. They include such things as size or weight, geometry or the number of teeth in a gear, the number of coils in a spring, or the number of tubes in a heat exchanger. In short, they represent any number of variables that may be required to quantify or completely describe an engineering system. The number of variables depends upon the type of the design involved, and as it increases, so does the complexity of the solution to the design problem.

OBJECTIVE FUNCTION

The process of selecting the "best solution" from various possible solutions must be based on a prescribed criterion, which is the **objective function**. For the purpose of optimization , the objective function is defined as a mathematical equation that embodies the design variables to be minimized or maximized. It can be given in the form

$$\mathbf{D} = f(\mathbf{x}) \tag{11.1}$$

D is used here to show that a desired effect is to be achieved. The variables $\mathbf{x} = (x_1, x_2, \ldots, x_n)$ represent the design variables.

CONSTRAINTS

In many engineering situations, the designer is often not free to do what he or she chooses, for any of several reasons. For example, in the design of thermal systems requiring high temperature conditions, a designer is limited because there are few materials that are able to withstand high temperatures. Another source of restrictions is economics considerations. The engineer/designer must learn to operate within such restrictions; in the field of optimization, these are termed **constraints**.

DESIGN SPACE

The total region, or domain, defined by all the design variables in the objective function is called the **design space**. This is normally limited by constraints (see Figure 11.1); otherwise, we might have an unbounded design space for which no feasible solution may exist. Therefore, the use of constraints is especially useful in restricting the region in which to search for the desired optimum values of the design variables.

The set of all points which satisfy both the equality and the inequality constraints is known as the **feasible region** of the objective function f(**x**). The vector **x** in the feasible region is called a **feasible point**. A feasible point can be either at the interior of the feasible region or at its boundary. Optimization involves the selection of the best feasible point that satisfies the objective function.

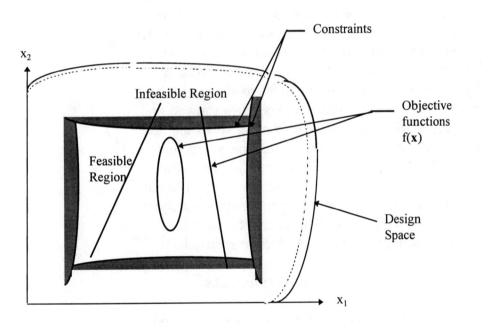

Figure 11.1 Definition of design space

11.3 METHOD OF SOLUTIONS

One of the most difficult aspects of optimization is how to obtain an acceptable solution. There are several methods of obtaining solutions, but they are beyond the scope of this book. However, to demonstrate how solutions may be obtained, a special class of optimization problems called **single variable** optimization problems is given here. It is so called because the objective function is a function of a single variable.

GRAPHICAL SOLUTION

The easiest approach for solving single variable optimization is to graph the function f(x). The variable x is plotted in the horizontal axis while f(x) is plotted on the vertical axis. From the graph the best value of the function can be obtained by visual inspection. Of course the solution obtained for some functions may depend on the range of values used in graphing the problem.

SEARCH METHODS

Another approach for solving single-variable optimization problems is by the use of the Search Method. This method is suitable for computer application. It is based on evaluating the objective function, f(x), at a sequence of points x_1, x_2, ...,x_k and comparing values in order to reach the optimal solution x*. The search method can be understood by considering the following scenario. Suppose that you are blind-folded and put in an empty room and you are told that somewhere in the room is a check for you in the amount of one million dollars. How can you find it? One way may be to begin at one corner of the room and take sequential steps in a straight line making sure that you do not leave any space between successive steps until you reach the end of the other corner and turn around making sure you do not retrace the path you followed before. If you are systematic you will eventually step on the check. This in effect is what the search method does, only using a more efficient approach.

PRINCIPLES OF SINGLE VARIABLE SEARCH TECHNIQUES.

The more efficient techniques in the Single Search Method are applicable to the **unimodal functions**, one that possesses one hump or one depression within a defined interval (see Figure 11.2, note that in the first interval the function decreases up to point 1, thereafter increases).

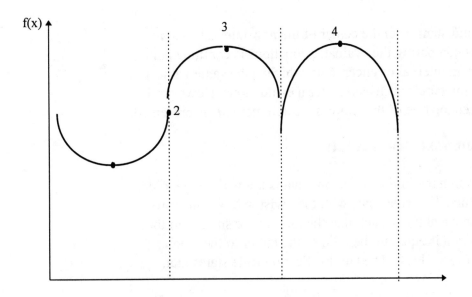

Figure 11.2   Illustration of unimodal functions

To illustrate these principles, it is assumed that the functions
are unimodal functions. Consider two points x_1 and x_2 on the
interval [a, b], at which the objective function is to be evaluated.
Since we want to confine our search in the [a, b] region, this
bounded region is called the **initial interval of uncertainty** and
is shown in Figure 11.3. Also shown in Figure 11.3 is $f(x_1)$
and $f(x_2)$. Suppose that the maximum is to be found.

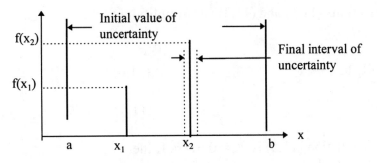

Figure 11.3 Illustrations of definitions used in a search method.

The two functions, $f(x_1)$ and $f(x_2)$ are compared. Since $f(x_2)$ >
$f(x_1)$, the region between point a and x_1 is discarded.   The
solution x^*, must lie between x_1 and b.   Next, we must
determine how to select the next point for evaluation and
comparison. There are several possible methods used. One
method is to divide the interval into two parts and place two

points equidistant from the center of the new interval. This process of comparing the evaluated functions is continued until we obtain an interval of uncertainty which is the same value as a specified tolerance; such as ε, after n evaluations. However, in the next section one of the simplest search methods is presented.

11.4 GOLDEN SECTION SEARCH

This search method is based on what is known as the Golden Section Rule. This rule deals with the division of an interval into two unequal parts, such that the ratio of the smaller to the larger interval is equal to the ratio of the larger to the whole. Consider Figure 11.4. The Golden Section Rule states that,

$$R_2/R_1 = R_1/R \tag{11.2}$$

but

$$R = R_1 + R_2 \tag{11.3}$$

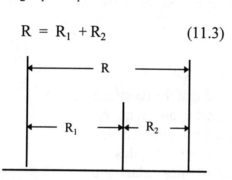

Figure 11.4 Golden section rule

Combining the two equations (11.2) and (11.3) and simplifying gives;

$$(R_2/R_1)^2 + R_2/R_1 = 1 \tag{11.4}$$

Let $K = R_2/R_1$

then

$$K^2 + K = 1 \tag{11.5}$$

The positive solution to equation (11.5) is $K = 0.6180$. If the Golden Section Rule is applied in a search, the interval of uncertainty is reduced by the value of $K = 0.6180$. By repeated applications of the rule, the interval of uncertainty, after "n" evaluations, is related to the initial value of uncertainty by the equation:

$$I_n = I_0 (0.6180)^{n-1} \tag{11.6}$$

where

$\quad I_n = $ The interval of uncertainty after
$\qquad$ n evaluations,

$\quad I_0 = $ initial interval of uncertainty,

n = number of evaluations.

The Golden Section Search Method is illustrated in Figure 11.5.

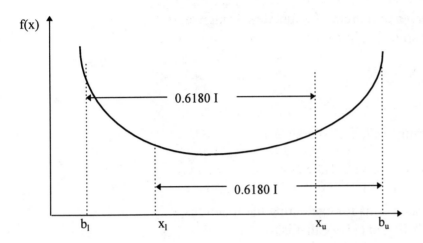

Figure 11. 5 Illustration of Golden section search method

Let the boundaries of the region of search be denoted b_l for the lower boundary and b_u for the upper boundary. Therefore the interval for the search, I, is given as:

$$I = b_u - b_l \qquad (11.7)$$

The question remains where to place the first point. Using the Golden Section Rule, the point must be placed then at point x_u, such that $x_u = 0.6180I$ from b_l. Since a Search Method involves comparison of two values, another point is required. This second point must be placed so that the interval of uncertainty is the same from the other end (see Figure 11.5), therefore, we place the point at x_l, which is also 0.6180I from the upper boundary b_u. The function can be evaluated at the two points. Then we make a comparison to see if $f(x_l) < f(x_u)$ (for minimization). If this is so, then the search is confined to the region left of $x = x_l$; otherwise the search is confined to the right of $x = x_u$. A new interval of uncertainty is defined, using the same approach as in the first case. The process of evaluation is continued until an interval of uncertainty is obtained that is equal to the desired tolerance.

Before we give a step-by-step procedure for conducting the Golden Section Search technique, note from Figure 11.5 that

$$x_l = b_u - KI \qquad (11.8)$$

$$x_u = b_l + KI \qquad (11.9)$$

where,

K = 0.6180

The steps for finding a minimum of a function, using the Golden Section Rule, are:

Step 1

Input $b_{l,1}$, $b_{u,1}$, K, function f, and tolerance ε .

Step 2

Define the two initial points for evaluating the functions, using equations (11.8) and (11.9); that is:

$$x_{l,1} = b_{u,1} - KI, \qquad (11.10)$$

$$x_{u,1} = b_{l,1} + KI, \qquad (11.11)$$

(Note $I_1 = bu_1 - bl_1$)

Set n = 1.

Step 3

Make a comparison of the values to determine the interval which contains the desired minimum:

If $f(x_{l,n}) \le f(x_{u,n})$ set;

$$b_{l,n+1} = b_{l,n} \qquad\qquad (11.12)$$

$$b_{u,n+1} = x_{u,n} \qquad\qquad (11.13)$$

$$I_{n+1} = b_{u,n+1} - b_{l,n+1} \qquad\qquad (11.14)$$

$$x_{l,n+1} = b_{u,n+1} - KI_{n+1} \qquad\qquad (11.15)$$

$$x_{u,n+1} = x_{l,n} \qquad\qquad (11.16)$$

go to step 5. Otherwise, go to step 4.

Step 4

Update information for the next search by setting

$$b_{l,n+1} = x_{l,n} \qquad\qquad (11.17)$$

$$b_{u,n+1} = b_{u,n} \qquad\qquad (11.18)$$

$$I_{n+1} = b_{u,n+1} - b_{l,n+1} \qquad\qquad (11.19)$$

$$x_{l,n+1} = x_{u,n} \qquad\qquad (11.20)$$

$$x_{u,n+1} = b_{l,n+1} + KI_{n+1} \qquad\qquad (11.21)$$

Step 5

Test to see if a satisfactory level of tolerance has been achieved.
If $|b_{u,n} - b_{l,n}| \le \varepsilon$ go to step 6. Otherwise set $n = n + 1$ and return to step 3.

Step 6

Output the solution as follows:
$x^* = \min\{x_{l,n}, x_{u,n}\}$ and $f_{min} = \min\{f(x_{l,n}), f(x_{u,n})\}$.

The above steps can be used for finding the maximum by modifying the test condition in step 3. A detailed algorithm for writing a computer program is given in Figure 11.6 and a sample program is listed in Appendix F.

Example 11.1
Determine the maximum value of the function $f(x) = x\cos\pi\, x^2$ in the interval [0.0, 0.7]. Use $\varepsilon = 1 \times 10^{-4}$.

Solution I - Golden Section method

Step 1
$b_{l,1} = 0.0 : \quad b_{u,1} = 0.7 : \quad I_1 = 0.7$
$f(x) = x\cos\pi\, x^2$
$\varepsilon = 1 \times 10^{-4}$.
The above input satisfies step 1.
Step 2
Define the two initial points, using equations (11.10) and (11.11);
$x_{l,1} = 0.7 - (0.6180)(0.7) = 0.2674$

$$x_{u,1} = 0.0 + (0.6180)(0.7) = 0.4326.$$

Step 3

Determine the interval which contains the maximum;

f(0.26740) = 0.2606

f(0.4326) = 0.3600. Since f(0.4326) > f(0.2674), the region of interest must lie between $x_{l,1}$ and $b_{u,1}$. We go to step 4 and update the various variables.

Step 4

Using equations (11.17) through (11.21); set

$b_{l,2} = x_{l,1} = 0.2674, b_{u,2} = b_{u,1} = 0.7$

$I_2 = 0.4326, x_{l,2} = x_{u,1} = 0.4326$

$x_{u,2} = b_{l,2} + KI_2 = 0.5347$

Step 5

Test whether the tolerance is satisfied. $|0.7| > \varepsilon$, so we increase n to 2 and return to step 3. The results for some subsequent iterations are given in Table 11.1. The final solution after 20 iterations is: x* = 0.4562 and f_{max} = 0.3622.

Table 11.1 Partial Iteration results for Example 11.1

Iter	b_l	b_u	x_l	x_u	$f(x_l)$	$f(x_u)$
1	0.0000	0.7000	0.2674	0.4326	0.2607	0.3599
3	0.2674	0.5347	0.3695	0.4326	0.3360	0.3599
6	0.4326	0.4957	0.4567	0.4716	0.3620	0.3610
9	0.4475	0.4624	0.4532	0.4567	0.3620	0.3620
12	0.4532	0.4567	0.4545	0.4554	0.3620	0.3620
15	0.4554	0.4562	0.4557	0.4559	0.3620	0.3620
19	0.4559	0.4560	0.4559	0.4559	0.3620	0.3620

Solution II - Graphical

The function is graphed as solution in Figure 11.7, from which the optimum is obtained as:

$$x^* = 0.45$$

$$f(x) = 0.36$$

Note however, that the graphical solution is not as accurate as the Golden section result due to difficulties always associated with graphical solutions.

Algorithm Golden

0. **Input** search limits bl, bu , f(x), ε
1. **If** problem is minimization →
2.   sig:= -1
3. **Else**
4.   sig:= 1
5. **End If**
6. r:= 0.6180: Δb:= bu - bl
7. xl:= bu -rΔb : xu:= bl + r Δb
8. **Do** while Δb > ε
9.   **If** (-sig*f(xl)   (-sig*f(xu)) →
10.   bu:= xu: xu:= xl
11.   Δb:= bu - bl: xl:= bu - r Δb
12.   **Else**
13.   bl:= xl: xl:= xu
14.   Δb:= bu - bl: xu:= bl + r Δb
15.   **End if**
16. **End loop**
17. **If** xl > xu→
18.   x:= xl
19. **Else**
20.   x:= xu
21. **End if**
22. **Output** x, f(x)
    End Algorithm

Figure 11.6. Algorithm for Golden Section
Search Method.

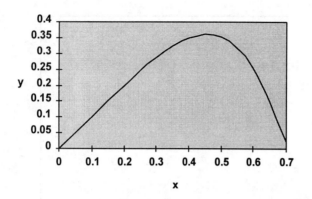

Figure 11.7 Graphical solution or example 11.1

Example 11.2

A man wants to set up a tent, for a big indoor rally, with the geometry of a right pyramid. The floor space available for this project is 120 m². The height of the tent is 8 m. How must he select the dimensions of the base for a minimum surface area? The door to the tent takes up 21 m².

Solution

Using the engineering approach to problem solving, the solution is presented as:

Find: length (l) and width (w)
Given: Floor area (A) = 120 m², height (h) = 8 m
    door area = 21 m²

Theory: Surface area (S) of a right pyramid is:

$$S = l\sqrt{h^2 + (w/h)^2} + w\sqrt{h^2 + (l/2)^2}$$

Base area is
    A = wl

Assumption: Assume that floor area is all utilized

Solution format for optimization:
    Because of the assumption
        wl = 120
    express l in terms of w, l = 120/w

The surface area in terms of w is given as:

$$S = \frac{120\sqrt{h^2 + (w/2)^2}}{w} + w\sqrt{h^2 + (60/w)^2} - 21$$

The problem is put in the form:

Minimize S

Subject to $0 \leq w \leq 120$

Note that the constraint on w is based on the size of the floor. Since there is uncertainty as to where the value of w lies, it assumed that the worst case is for w to be 120. Using the Golden Search program (included) in this book the solution obtained is as follows: w = 10.9544 m, l = 10.9545 m, S = 191.4147 m^2.

SOURCE USED

Onwubiko, C., **Foundations of Computer-Aided Design**,
West Publishing Co., St. Paul, Minnesota, 1989.

PROBLEMS

11.1. Maximize the function $f(x) = x^3 + 6x^2 - 4x - 8$. Search for the solution in the range $-2 \le x \le 2$.

11.2. What is the minimum value of the function

$$y = x^2(e^{-x} + \cos x) \quad \text{in the following intervals:}$$

(a) $1.75 \le x \le 3.25$

(b) $3.5 \le x \le 5.25$

Is the solution you obtained the true minimum? If not, why is your solution not correct, and what should be the correct one?

(Hint: Examine the interval $3.75 \le x \le 5.25$.)

11.3. Maximize the function

$$y = (0.92 - 0.4 \sin \theta)^2 + (0.34 + 0.4 \cos \theta)^2. \text{ Use}$$

a tolerance of .000001. Does the selection of interval of search affect the maximum obtained? Graph the function to validate your solution.

11.4. It is desired to fabricate a V-shaped watering trough by joining four pieces of metal of uniform thickness (Fig.P11.4). Formulate the objective function in terms of the missing dimension for a maximum volume. What is the value of the missing dimension?. Using differential calculus or any other similar method, verify your solution.

Fig.P11.4

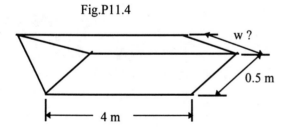

11.5 A farmer wishes to fence a grazing field for his cattle. On one side of the field is a pond for the cattle and it has a straight edge. If he has 1 200 m of fencing material, what is the area of the largest rectangular area he can fence ?

11.6 Find the volume of the largest right circular cylinder that can be inscribed in a sphere of radius 1.5 m.

NOTES

CHAPTER 12

DECISION TOOL- ENGINEERING ECONOMY

12.1 INTRODUCTION

Engineers often find themselves in management positions that require business decisions, therefore, the engineer must have some basic knowledge of the financial consequences of any decision. Furthermore, the nature of engineering, at the present time, demands that an engineer must consider also the economic benefits in making design decisions. For example, in the conceptual design phase, if the engineer is to decide between two or more alternative solutions for a component of a machine, one factor that must be considered is the cost of producing the parts. This requires some knowledge of engineering economy. Another situation may arise where an engineer in a management position may have to decide whether it is preferable to purchase a machine to produce a one time product or simply to lease the machine. These types of decisions require economic analysis.

The examples used in this chapter are first general nature and then specific to engineering applications. The rationale is that the principles are the same, therefore, a student mastering the general examples will easily understand how to apply these principles to engineering type problems.

12.2 RETURN ON CAPITAL

The primary goal of any business endeavor is to obtain a return or profit on the capital invested. In a broad sense capital consists of money, property and other resources used in the operation of the business. Basically, there are two kinds of capital: **equity** and **borrowed**. Equity capital is that owned by the individuals who have invested some money or property with the hope of obtaining a return (or profit). Borrowed capital is obtained from lenders such as the banks. A business that operates on a borrowed capital must strive to make enough profit so that after paying off the interest to the lender a sizable profit is still realized.

Profit is the difference between income and costs. One thing that must be considered as a part of the cost is the interest paid on a borrowed capital. Regardless of the type of capital used in a business, the primary concern is the rate of return on the investment. The rate of return is profit divided by investment, that is,

Annual rate of return = annual profit/invested capital

The rate of return is a primary consideration in the investment of any capital. Therefore, an engineer must consider this factor before embarking on any capital intensive project. The return on capital is time dependent hence consideration must be given to the time value of capital.

12.3 TIME VALUE OF MONEY

It was not too long ago when with one dollar one could buy two loaves of bread, but today one can hardly buy a loaf of bread with a dollar. On the other hand, if a dollar had been deposited into an account when the cost of a loaf of bread was fifty cents, that dollar will have earned interest so that the value of it today is greater than when it was deposited. This idea that a dollar in the present time is not equal to a dollar in the future because it could earn interest when placed on a deposit, is known as the **time value of money**. Interest is the cost of using money. If someone deposits money in the bank it is used by the bank and in return the bank pays the person interest. On the other hand, if one obtains a loan from the bank the person must pay back the original capital plus some charges the bank levies on the individual for using its money that it could have invested in some other profit making venture. There are two kinds of interest: **simple** and **compound.**

SIMPLE INTEREST

If the interest charged is applied to the principal amount borrowed then the interest is said to be simple. The simple interest, I, is

$$I = Pni \qquad (12.1)$$

where,

  $P =$ the principal amount (lent or borrowed)
  $n =$ number of interest periods
  $i =$ interest rate per interest period.

The total amount paid back at the end of the interest period is $P + I$. Using (12.1), the total amount, S_n, paid back is

$$S_n = P(1 + ni) \qquad\qquad (12.2)$$

Example 12.1

A man borrows $10 000 at an annual interest of 9 percent with the entire amount due in three years. How much must he pay at the end of the period?

Solution

Using (12.2)
$$S = 10\ 000(1 + 3(0.09)) = \$12\ 700$$
The man repays $12 700 at the end of the three year period.

COMPOUND INTEREST

When the interest charged is based not only on the original principal but on the interest due but not yet paid, the interest is said to be calculated based on compound interest. Using the same notation as before, the amount paid back at the end of first interest period is

$$S_1 = P + I_1 = P(1+i)$$

In the second interest period

$$S_2 = S_1 + I_2 = S_1 + S_1 i = P(1+i) + Pi(1+i) = P(1+i)^2$$

In the third interest period

$$S_3 = S_2 + I_3 = S_2 + S_2 i = P(1+i)^2 + P(1+i)^2 i$$

$$S_3 = P(1+i)^2(1 + i) = P(1+i)^3$$

In general, the amount paid at the end of the nth period is

$$S_n = P(1+i)^n \qquad\qquad (12.3)$$

where,

S_n = total sum of money at the end of n period.

Example 12.2

Repeat example 12.2 if the interest is compounded quarterly.
Solution

$i = 0.09/4 = 0.0225$
$n = 4$ compoundings/year x 3 years $= 12$
From (12.3)
$$S_{12} = 10\ 000(1 + 0.0225)^{12} = 13\ 061$$
Therefore, the pay back amount is $13 061.

DISCOUNTING THE FUTURE

It is often necessary to determine what funds must be invested now to obtain a future sum. This means the evaluation of a future value at the present time. In doing this the inverse of the right hand side of equation (12.3) is applied. Suppose it is desired that the amount S_n be received after n periods at the interest rate of i%, the amount P that must be invested now is obtained from equation (12.3) as

$$P = \frac{S_n}{(1 + i)^n} \qquad (12.4)$$

The denominator of equation (12.4) is known as **single payment present worth factor.**

Example 12.3

During your first year in college an uncle promises to give you $20 000 so you can go into business for yourself 6 years after you graduate from college. If the interest rate is 7½% and compounded quarterly, how much must he invest in your freshman year, if it is assumed that the graduation time is five years.

Solution

$n = 4$ compounding/year x 11 years $= 44$
$i = 0.075/4 = 0.01875$
From (12.4)
$$P = 20\ 000/(1+0.01875)^{44} = 8\ 831.91$$
The uncle must invest $8 831.91 at your freshman year.

CASH FLOW DIAGRAMS

The following discussion can be simplified by the use of cash flow diagrams. Their use makes it easier to visualize what happens in any financial transaction that involves cash inflow and outflow. The cash flow diagram basically consists of a horizontal line and series of vertical pointing arrows. The horizontal line depicts a time scale subdivided into intervals of periods of the time involved. The arrow indicates whether money is coming in or going out. An arrow pointing downwards indicates cash outflow whereas an upward pointing arrow indicates cash inflow. It should be noted that the cash flow diagram is dependent on the viewpoint (lender or borrower) from which it is constructed. This can be seen from the cash flow diagram of example 12.2 shown in Figure 12.1. Note that the periods are labeled in the intervals instead of the end of a period.

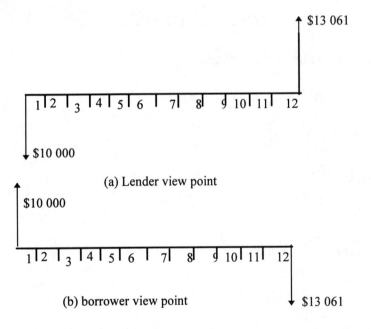

Figure 12.1 Cash flow diagram for example 12.2

ANNUITIES

When the term annuity is used, it often reminds one of planning for retirement. Annuity is defined as an amount of money that is payable to a beneficiary at regular interval for a prescribed period of time from a reserved sum of money. Another way to view it is to consider a target sum of money and raise the question what should be the amount of a series of deposits made at a given equally spaced time periods to attain the target amount?

Suppose that the future amount is denoted by S_n and the amount deposited at the end of each period is, A, at an interest rate of i%, it is easy to derive the relationship between this sum of money and the periodic deposit, A. It should be realized that the last deposited amount does not earn any interest so its contribution to the sum S_n is A. The second to the last earns the interest Ai and contributes $A + Ai$ (or $A(1 + i)$) to S_n. The first deposit at the end of the nth period has earned interest for a total period of n-1. Using (12.3) its contribution to S_n is $A(1+i)^{n-1}$, S_n can be written as:

$$S_n = A(1+i)^{n-1} + A(1+i)^{n-2} + \ldots A(1+i) + A \quad (12.5)$$

Multiply both sides of (12.5) by (1+i) to obtain

$$(1+i)S_n = A(1+i)^n + A(1+i)^{n-1} + \ldots A(1+i)^2 + A(1+i) \quad (12.6)$$

Subtracting (12.6) from (12.5) gives

$$S_n - (1+i)S_n = A(1 - (1+i)^n)$$
or
$$-iS_n = A(1 - (1+i)^n)$$

by multiplying both sides by -1 we have

$$s_n = A\left[\frac{(1 + i)^n - 1}{i}\right] \quad (12.7)$$

The term in the bracket is often termed **the uniform series compound factor.**

The inverse of (12.7) is

$$A = S_n \left[\frac{i}{(1 + i)^n - 1} \right] \qquad (12.8)$$

Example 12.4

A man begins at his thirtieth birthday to deposit $120 at the end of each month in a bank that pays 8% annually interest. If the interest is compounded monthly, how much will he have at his fiftieth birthday.

Solution

n = 12 compoundings/year x 20 years = 240
i = 0.08/12 = 0.0067
From (12.7) we have
$S_{240} = 120[((1 + 0.0067)^{240} - 1)/0.0067] = 71\ 034.83$
The man will have $71 034.83 at his fiftieth birthday.

CAPITAL RECOVERY

Examination of equations (12.4) and (12.7) indicates that the two equations can easily be combined. An annuity has a future lump sum, S_n. This future sum must also have an equivalent present value P. Therefore, it is logical to think of P as being, in concept, equivalent to the present worth of the future value of S_n. This relation is shown in cash flow diagram Figure 12.2. By combining (12.4) and (12.7) we have

$$P = A \left[\frac{(1 + i)^n - 1}{i(1 + i)^n} \right] \qquad (12.9)$$

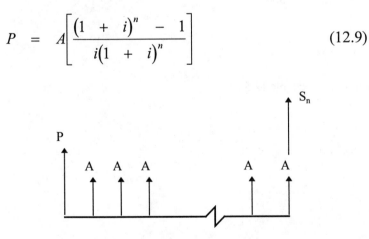

Figure 12.2 A cash flow diagram relating present
worth P and annuity S_n

It is often necessary to solve for A in (12.9) giving,

$$A = P\left[\frac{i(1 + i)^n}{(1 + i)^n - 1}\right]$$ (12.10)

The term in the bracket in (12.10) is known as the **capital recovery factor** or **the uniform annual payment annuity factor**. As the name suggests, equation (12.10) is useful in computing installment loans repayment plan.

Example 12.5

A man borrows $110 000 from a mortgage company at annual interest rate of 9% compounded monthly. The loan is to be repaid in 30 years. What is the monthly payment on this loan?

Solution

$n = 12$ compoundings/year x 30 years = 360
$i = 0.09/12 = 0.0075$

From (12.10)

$A = 110\ 000[(.0075(1 + 0.0075)^{360})/((1 + 0.0075)^{360} - 1)]$
$= 885.08$

The monthly payment is $885.08. The cash flow diagram for this problem from the lender's view point is shown in Figure 12.3

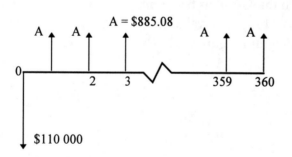

Figure 12.3 Cash flow diagram for Example 12.5

12.3 EVALUATION OF ALTERNATIVES

In the previous section the time value of money was examined. From this concept it is clear that time and interest rate affect any capital. Ultimately, the investment of any capital is aimed at profit making and therefore care must be exercised in committing capital to any project. In many situations, companies commit capital to purchase the necessary equipment for manufacturing a given product. The normal practice is to consider equipment from various manufacturers. The problem is made more difficult by the fact that some equipment may have an initial high cost and a low maintenance cost while another may have an initial low cost but high maintenance cost. How one decides on which alternative to choose is the subject of this section. There are two ways of approaching this problem. The first is the **equivalent worth** method and the second is **the rate of return method**. In the first method all cash flow is reduced to an equivalent worth at some point in time using an interest rate judged to be the minimum attractive rate of return (MARR).

The second method calculates the annual rate of profit or savings resulting from an investment. This rate of return is of course compared to MARR. The two methods are related, however, only the approaches in the equivalent worth method are discussed. But before discussing these methods, certain terms are defined.

Investment Cost

This is the initial amount of purchase price and of installment of the assets.

Salvage (Residual) Value

Salvage or Residual value is a realistic estimate of the net sum realized due to the disposal of an item or property when it is no longer needed.

Life

Life or economic life is a numerical value in units of time (usually years) that the user expects an item or property to be used.

PRESENT WORTH (PW)

Present worth is the amount of money that must be invested at the present (now) to produce a determined sum at a future date. In the present worth method all future projected cash inflows and outflows are converted to a single present value at a time zero. In this method it is assumed that the interest rate is equal to MARR.

Example 12.7

A machine shop is considering purchasing a CNC machine at an initial price of $45 650. It is estimated that the machine will yield an annual revenue of $7 300 for six years. Then the shop will resell the machine for $23 650. The yearly operation and maintenance cost is $2 100. The machine shop has determined that its MARR is 10%, before income taxes, on all invested capital. Should the machine shop purchase this machine?

Solution

The present worth of annual revenue is computed using (12.9).

A = 7 300, i = 0.1, n = 6,

$$P = 7300\left[\frac{(1+0.1)^6 - 1}{0.1(1+0.1)^6}\right] = 31\ 793.40$$

The present worth of the operation and maintenance cost is determined in the same fashion

$$P = 2100\left[\frac{(1+0.1)^6 - 1}{0.1(1+0.1)^6}\right] = 9\ 146.05$$

The present worth of the resale value is computed using (12.4);

$$P = 23\ 650/(1+0.1)^6 = 13\ 349.81$$

The solution is now summarize based on present worth as follows:

Description	Cash outflow	Cash inflow
Initial machine cost	- $45 650	
Annual revenue		$31 793.40
Operation and Maint.	- $9 146.05	
Resale value (Salvage)		$13 349.81
Total	- $54 796.05	$45 143.21

The net present worth is -$54 796.05 + $45 143.21 = -$9 652.84. Since the net worth is a negative quantity the machine should not be purchased.

FUTURE WORTH (FW)

The future worth method is similar in concept to the present worth method. The only difference is that in the future worth method all cash inflows and out flows are computed based on a future time.

Example 12.8
Repeat problem 12.7 using the future worth method.

Solution
The future worth of initial cost using (12.3) as

FW of Initial cost = $45 650 $(1 + 0.1)^6$ = $80 871.76
FW of Annual Revenue by (12.7) is

$$FW \ of \ Re venue \ = \ 7300\left[\frac{(1 + 0.1)^6 - 1}{0.1}\right] \ = \ 56 \ 323.95$$

Similarly FW of operation and maintenance is:

$$2 \ 100\{(1.1)^6 - 1\}/0.1 = \$16 \ 202.78$$

The solution is now summarized based on future worth as follows:

Description	Cash outflow	Cash inflow
Initial machine cost	-$80 871.76	
Annual revenue		$56 323.95
Operation and Maint.	- $16 202.78	
Resale value (Salvage)		$23 650
Total	- $97 074.54	$79 973.95

The net future worth is -$97 074.54 + $79 973.95 =
-$17 100.59. Since the net worth is a negative quantity the
machine should not be bought.

ANNUAL WORTH (AW)

The annual worth method is similar in principle to the two
previous methods. The only difference is that it converts the
cash inflow and cash outflow of either the present worth or
future worth into an annuity. In equation form it is written as

$$AW = CI - CO - CR \qquad (12.11)$$

where,
   CI = annual cash inflows
   CO = annual cash outflows
   CR = annual capital recovery

Annual capital recovery may be computed using

$$CR = P_o \left[\frac{i(1+i)^n}{(1+i)^n - 1} \right] - S \left[\frac{i}{(1+i)^n - 1} \right] \qquad (12.12)$$

where,
   P_o = Initial investment value
   S = Salvage value or resale value.

Example 12.9
   Repeat Example 12.7 using the annual worth method.
Solution

The revenue and the operating and maintenance values are

already in annual basis, therefore we simply compute CR using (12.12).

$$CR = 45\ 650\{.1(1+.1)^6)/((1.1)^6 - 1)\} - 23\ 650\ (.1/(1.1)^6 - 1)$$
$$= 10\ 481.58 - 3\ 065.21 = 7\ 416.37$$

Applying (12.11)

$$AW = \$7\ 300 - \$2\ 100 - \$7\ 416.37 = -\$2\ 216.37$$

Again because AW < 0 the machine should not be purchased.

All the three methods lead to the same conclusion although the numerical values are different. Therefore, it really does not matter which method is selected. However, many people prefer the annual worth method because it lends itself to easy interpretation since most people work with annual income and annual expenditures.

12.4 DEPRECIATION

The term "wear and tear" is a well known one. Whenever any physical property is in use it either wears out or becomes obsolete. As a result, over a period of time, the value of the property decreases. This reduction in value is known as **depreciation**. Depreciation is important in the decision making related to any project for at least two reasons. First, it allows the depreciation (which is a loss) to be considered as a part of production cost when a particular piece of equipment is used. Second, it provides a means of recovery of the initial cost of a physical property. From the first reason, it can be realized that unless depreciation is taken into consideration for accounting purposes a company may be paying higher taxes than it should because of not considering loss of value from the depreciation of its physical property.

Depreciation is generally classified into two major categories: **normal depreciation** and **depreciation due to price changes**. A normal depreciation is that associated with either the inability of the physical property to produce results or the obsolescence of the physical property. Regardless of the category, the accounting principles for handling depreciation remains virtually unchanged although depreciation methods have often been changed because of income taxes. The most commonly used methods are discussed below.

STRAIGHT-LINE DEPRECIATION

This method of depreciation allocates equal part of the depreciable cost to each period of the depreciable life or economic life of the physical property. It is simply and widely used. Its use involves the following:

$$d = \frac{P - SV}{n} \qquad (12.13)$$

$$D_t = \frac{t(P - SV)}{n} \qquad (12.14)$$

where,

P = Initial investment cost of the asset
SV = Salvage value
n = depreciable life of the asset
d = annual depreciation deduction
D_t = cumulated depreciation through period t
t = time period.

Often it becomes necessary to determine the book value (the difference between initial cost and accumulated depreciation) of an asset and this is computed using

$$BV_t = P - D_t \qquad (12.15)$$

where,

BV_t = book value at time t

Example 12.10

A company purchased a delivery truck for $17 600 and expects to trade it in at the end of 5th year. The trade-in value is estimated at $3 200. What is the depreciation cost that should be deducted in the company's income tax in the first year? What is the book value of the truck at the end of the third year?

Solution

P = 17 600; SV = 3 200 ; n = 5; t = 3
From (12.13)
    d = (17 600 - 3 200)/5 = 2 880
Using (12.14) and (12.15)

$$BV_t = 17\ 600 - 3(17\ 600 - 3\ 200)/5$$
$$= \$8\ 960$$

The amount to be deducted from the income tax is \$2 880 and the book value of the truck at the end of the third year is \$8 960.

SUM-OF-THE-YEARS'-DIGITS METHOD (SYD)

Unlike the straight-line method, the SYD assigns larger depreciation amount in the earlier years and smaller amounts in the later years of the depreciable life. It is computed using

$$d_t \;=\; (P \;-\; SV)\frac{2(n \;-\; t \;+\; 1)}{n(n \;+\; 1)} \qquad (12.16)$$

where,
d_t = depreciation value for period t.

Example 12.11
Repeat Example 12.10 by the SYD method.

Solution
With t = 1, from (12.16)
$$d_1 = (17\ 600 - 3\ 200)(2)(5 - 1 + 1)/5(5 + 1)$$
$$= 4\ 800$$
When t = 2
$$d_2 = 8(17\ 600 - 3\ 200)/30$$
$$= 3\ 840$$
At t = 3
$$d_3 = 6(17\ 600 - 3\ 200)/30$$
$$= 2\ 880$$

The total accumulated depreciation at the end of three years = 4 800 + 3 840 + 2 880 = 11 520. From (12.15) the book value at the end of the third year = 17 600 - 11 520 = 6 080.
Therefore, the depreciation to be deducted for income taxes for the first year is \$4 800 and the book value of the truck at the end of the third year is \$6 080.

THE DECLINING BALANCE METHOD

This method is also known as **Matheson formula** or the **constant percentage** method. The annual cost of depreciation is assumed to be a fixed percentage of the book value at the beginning of the year. If the fixed rate is denoted as k then the book value, BV_t, after a period t is computed using

$$BV_t = P(1 - k)^t \qquad (12.17)$$

where,

        k = a fixed rate (see eq. 12.20)
        P = investment cost of the asset
The allowable depreciation in period t is given by

$$d_t = kP(1 - k)^{t-1} \qquad (12.18)$$

If it is desirable to determine the cumulative depreciation at period t, it is obtained from

$$D_t = P[1 - (1 - k)^t] \qquad (12.19)$$

Note that unlike the two previous methods the allowable depreciation is independent of the salvage value. This means that a capital property can never depreciate to zero. This feature is the weakness of this method. This weakness is overcome by switching to any slower method of depreciation, such as the straight-line method, so that a zero or other book value may be obtained in year n. In equation form we can express

$$BV_n = P(1 - k)^n = SV$$

from which we can solve for k giving

$$k = 1 - (SV/P)^{1/n} \qquad (12.20)$$

Example 12.12
Repeat Example 12.10 using the declining balance method
Solution
    The constant rate k is computed from (12.20)
        $k = 1 - (3\ 200/17\ 600)^{1/5} = 0.29$
    Using (12.18)

$d_1 = 0.29(17\ 600) = 5\ 104.00$

Also from (12.17) , $BV_3 = 17\ 600(1 - 0.29)^3 = 6\ 299.23$

Hence, the amount of tax to be deducted in the first year is $5 104 and the book value of the truck at the end of the third year is $6 299.23.

SOURCES USED

DeGarmo, P.E., W. G. Sullivan, and J. Bontadelli,
Engineering Economy 8th ed. Macmillan, New York, 1989.

Kleinfeld, I. H. **Engineering and Managerial Economics,**
Holt, Rinehart and Winston, New York, 1986.

PROBLEMS

12.1   A young person in the tenth grade receives an inheritance of $15 600 from a grandparent. However, the stipulation is that this fund must be invested and can not be used until this person is a sophomore in college (4 years and 6 months later). The interest rate at the time of investment is 7.5%. How much money will this person have as a sophomore?

   (a) If the money is invested at simple interest
   (b) If the interest is compounded annually
   (c) If the interest is compounded semi-annually
   (d) If the interest is compounded monthly

12.2   You want to invest $18 500 for 4 years. The investment company offers you three choices. You can invest at the annual interest rate of 6% compounded either annually, semi annually or monthly. Which will you select and how much difference does your choice make compared to the next better option?

12.3   John's parents plan to buy him a car as a graduation gift from college. It is estimated that it will take him 5 years to graduate from an engineering college . The parents have also decided to buy a car that does not cost more than $25 000. How much must his parents invest now to reach this goal if the interest rate is 7.5% compounded semi-annually?

12.4   If an investment is to double in 5 years, what is the investment interest assuming quarterly compounding?

12.5   You have some money that you want to invest for 8 years. You have received two investment proposals: the first is for 6.7% annual interest compounded annually and the second is for 6.6 % annual interest compounded monthly. Which is a better deal?

12.6   The parents of a child decide to invest $115 monthly beginning with the child's first birthday celebration. How much money will the parents have for the child's college education during their child's eighteenth birth day celebration? Assume that the average annual interest is 7% compounded monthly. How much of this money is interest income?

12.7   You have two options: (a) Investing $720 annually at 6.5% for 10 years (b) Investing $60 monthly at the same interest rate and period but the investment is compounded monthly. Which will you choose and how much more money would you have for the choice you made?

12.8 Your parents agree to buy a car for you at graduation in next four and half years. However, they stipulate that you must pay the down payment for the car. If the car is expected to cost $25 000, and the bank is only willing to finance 80% of the cost, how much money must you save each month to attain this goal. Assume that your savings earn 6% annual interest compounded monthly. If the bank charges 11% annual interest and the loan is for five years, how much money must your parents increase their monthly budget to cover the cost of your car?

12.9 You have found a part time job that pays you a gross amount of $400 a month. You want a loan of $3000 from the bank for two and half years. The interest rate is 12%. The bank will deny the loan if your monthly payment is greater than 25% of the gross monthly income from your part time job. Will the bank approve your loan?

12.10 Your take home pay from a part-time job is $375 per month. How much are you able to borrow from a local bank at 14% for two years? To qualify for the loan, your monthly payment cannot exceed one-third of your take home pay.

12.11 Generate a table for the uniform series compound factor. The interest should range from 4 to 21% at an increment of 0.5%. The period in years should go from 5 to 20 at an increment of 5 years.

12.12 Generate a table of **capital recovery factor.** The interest rate should range from 8% to 11% at an increment of 1%. The period in months should range from 1 to 20 at the interval of one month.

12.13 A young engineer wants a mortgage loan of $130 000 to buy a house. The loan could be made for 15 years, 20 years or 30 years at an annual interest rate of 8.5%. If this individual has a budget of monthly mortgage of $1350.00, which option would you advise for this person. How much money over the entire life of the loan is saved by this person refusing the option that provides the least amount of monthly payment ?

12.14 A grandmother retires at the age of 65 years and dies at the age of 75 years. She withdraws $720 monthly from a savings account at an annual interest of 7.5%. If at her death she still had a balance of $100 000, what was the amount in her savings when she retired?

12.15 Two brothers receive a small machine shop from their father. The older brother offers to buy out the younger one by giving him either $20,000 cash now or paying him $510 per month for the next five years. Which offer should the younger brother accept?

12. 16   You graduate from engineering school at the age of 22 years. You want to retire at the age of 50 years. Thereafter you want to receive a monthly income of $3500 for the next 20 years from a mutual fund. How much money must you put in the mutual fund monthly to make this possible? Assume a constant annual interest of 9%.

12.17   A company is considering the purchase of two robotics welding machines. The initial cost of the first machine is $146 000 and that of the second is $130 000. Both machines will last for six years. The salvage value of the first machine is 20% of its original cost and that of the second is $23 500. The maintenance cost of the first machine is $150 monthly and that of the second is $3600 per annum payable at the end of the year. Which machine should the company purchase? Assume all interest rates are at 12% annually.

12.18   Repeat problem 12.17 using the Future worth method.

12.19   Solve problem 12.17 by the Annual worth method.

12.20   A company is considering the purchase of two production machines. The first machine costs $50 000 and it is estimated to last for 3 years. The cost for its replacement increases by 5% in every six months. The cost of maintenance is $1200 per year. Its salvage value is 10% of the initial cost. It is estimated to generate an annual revenue of $40 000. The cost of the second machine is $90 000 and it is estimated to last for 6 years. Its maintenance cost is estimated at $950 per year and will generate monthly revenue of $3 000. Its salvage value is estimated to be 15% of its original cost. Using the present worth method make a recommendation on which machine to purchase. Assume an annual interest of 12% is applicable.

12.21   Using the straight-line depreciation method, determine the condition under which both the salvage value and book value of a given item will be the same.

12.22   A bookkeeper using the straight-line depreciation determines that the book value of a piece of equipment after 8 years is $6 500 and the annual depreciation is 10% of the original cost. If the life of the equipment has been estimated at 10 years determine (a) the original cost of the equipment (b) its salvage value.

12.23   You want to buy a 3-year old car with an original cost of $21 560.   The owner had anticipated trading it in after using the car for 6 years. The owner was told at the time of purchase that in six years the car can be traded in for $5 400.   If a bank agrees to finance you for 80% of the book value of the car at 10% interest for 3 years, what will be your monthly payment? Assume that the straight-line depreciation method is applicable.

12.24   A company purchased a machine for $170 000 and expects it to be in use for 8 years. It is estimated that the salvage value will be 8% of the original cost.   What amount can the company depreciate against its taxable income in the second year? What is the book value of the machine at the end of the third year? Use the SYD method of depreciation

12.25 Repeat Problem 12.24 using the Declining Balance method.

12. 26 Write a program for computing the depreciation based on the three methods given in the text. The output should be the taxes payable at any period and the book value of the item. Verify your program using problem 12.24 but give the taxes to be paid in the first, third and sixth year and the book value in the same time period.

CHAPTER 13

PRESENTATION - GRAPHICAL COMMUNICATION

13.1 INTRODUCTION

A design is of no use unless it is properly communicated to those who must approve it and to those who must manufacture the various components of the design. Therefore, as an engineer one of the important things you do is to communicate your design to other technical people. Since engineers do not all speak the same language, it will be very difficult to communicate among engineers unless there is a common acceptable method of communication. Based on the saying " a picture is worth a thousand words," engineers communicate to each other in a graphical form. The graphical form used depends on what the engineer wants to communicate. One of the most important graphical forms is the engineering drawing. These are universally used to communicate manufacturing information in the form of lines, arcs, views, shapes and dimensions.

As an engineer you must communicate your design beginning from the conceptual phase to the definitive design using sketches or drawings, therefore, it is important that you acquire this communication skill. There are at least two reasons why you must acquire this skill. As an engineer you must communicate your design ideas to others in a very succinct manner. In addition, you may be responsible for reading and approving the drawings produced by a skilled drafts person. The manner in which the drawings are communicated remain the same, but the advances in computer technology have changed the medium of communicating these drawings. For example, the machine used to produce blue lines that led to the term "blueprint" for drawings are now being replaced by plotters, printers and various other methods of producing hard copies of drawings.

This chapter introduces the student to some of the important concepts in graphical communication. These include different types of graphs, method of sketching and the importance of geometric modeling in today's engineering practice.

13.2 GRAPHS

A graph is a visual representation of the relationship between various data. The most commonly encountered types of graphs are linear, bar and pie charts.

LINEAR GRAPHS

Linear graphs are useful in comparing or describing numerical data. They are useful in engineering experimentation because they help to establish the relationship between variables. For example, to discover the relationship between two variables, one variable, x , may be plotted on the horizontal axis or abscissa. The other, y, may be plotted on the ordinate or vertical axis. In engineering modeling, the most common assumed relationships are either linear or exponential. A linear model is represented by

$$y = ax + b \qquad (13.1)$$

An exponential model may be represented as

$$y = ax^b \qquad (13.2)$$

or

$$y = ae^{bx} \qquad (13.3)$$

The linear model, equation (13.1) and the exponential model may be plotted on graph papers.

The most common types of graph papers are the **rectangular** coordinate and the **logarithmic** (see Figure 13.1). In the rectangular coordinate paper the scales are arithmetic which means that the abscissa and the ordinate are divided into equal grids. The scales on logarithmic paper are logarithmic meaning that the divisions are such that they are based on the fact that the logarithm of any number is the power to which the base is raised to obtain the number. For example, the logarithm of 100 to base 10 is 2 because 10 raised to the power of 2 is 100. Therefore, the divisions in a logarithmic paper are not of equal spacing. Furthermore, the scale begins at 1 instead of zero. The commercially available logarithmic papers are of different forms and cycles. The one shown in Figure 13.1 has three cycles. Another graph paper is the **semi-logarithmic**. One of its axis is arithmetic while the other is logarithmic. Shown also in Figure 13.1 is a **Log-log** paper.

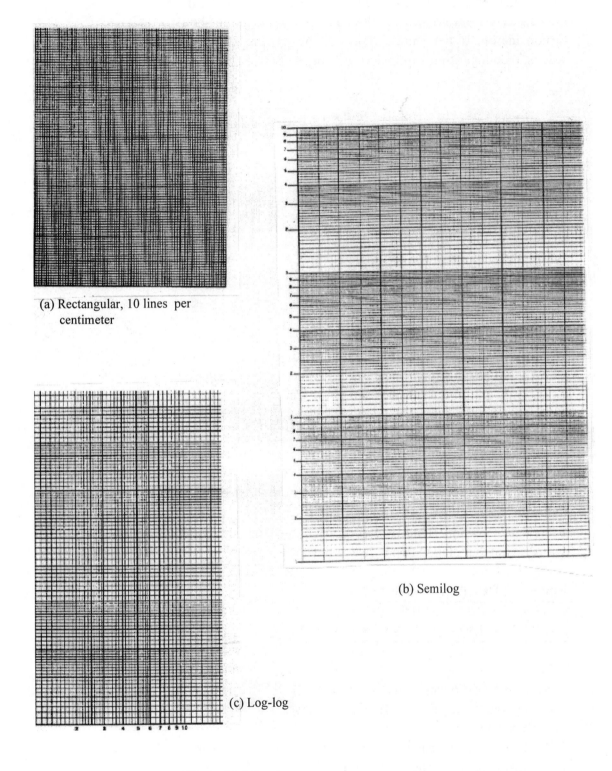

(a) Rectangular, 10 lines per
centimeter

(b) Semilog

(c) Log-log

Figure 13.1 Graph papers

You may wonder which of the graph papers that should be used in presenting your data. In most cases the rectangular graph paper is used. However, if the data varies from a very small value to a large value then the logarithmic type graphs should be used because less space is utilized. For example, if the values range from 0.01 to 1000, an logarithmic graph should be considered. If the data to be plotted contains negative values, then logarithmic graphs cannot be used.

Example 13.1
  Graph the data shown in Table 13.1

Table 13.1 Data for Example 13.1

x	12	16	18	20	26	37	50	68
y	100	200	270	300	500	1 000	2 000	3 000

Solution

  The data is plotted both on rectangular paper and semi-logarithmic paper as shown in Figures 13.2 and 13.3.
  It should be noted that linear graphs either on rectangular or logarithmic graph papers may be used for regression analysis of the form given in Chapter 10. This is illustrated in the next example.

Example 13.2
  The data shown in Table 13.2 is known to be exponential in nature. Find the relationship between the two variables.

Table 13.2 Data for Example 13.2

x	0.05	0.15	0.35	0.55	0.65	0.85	0.95	1.15
y	2.83	2.51	1.97	1.55	1.38	1.08	0.96	0.75

Solution
  Since the relationship must be of the form shown in equation (13.3), taking the logarithm of both sides gives:
$$\ln y = bx + \ln a$$
The values of b and a can be determined by plotting x versus y in a semi-log paper as shown in Figure 13.4.

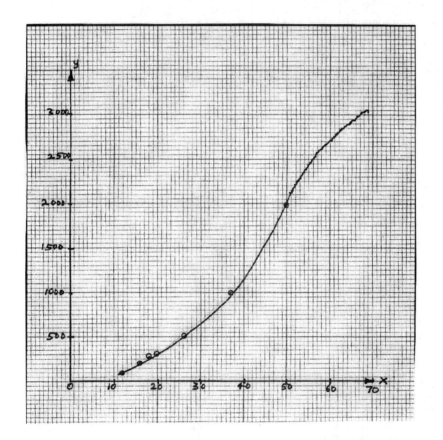

Figure 13.2 Data of Table 13.1 plotted
on a rectangular paper

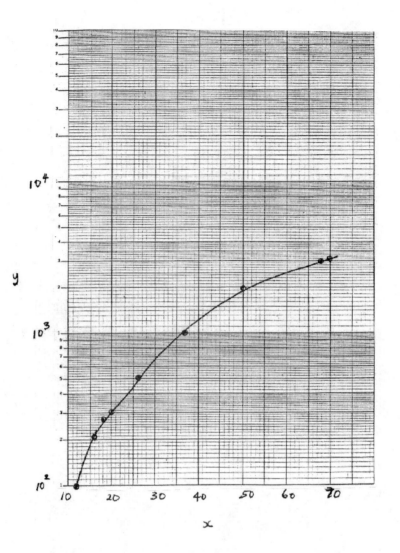

Figure 13.3. Data of Table 13.1 plotted on semi-log paper

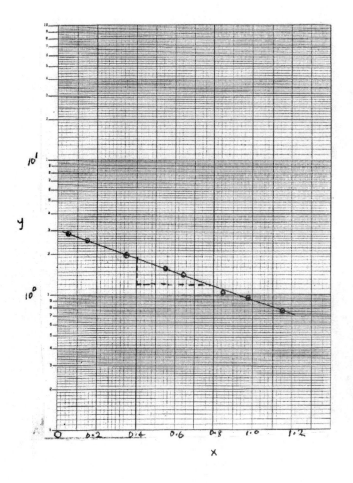

Figure 13.4 Plot for example 13.2

From the graph the following are obtained:
b = slope = Δy/Δx = (ln 1.9 - ln 1.18)/(0.4 - 0.8)   = -1.1908
intercept (i.e. where x = 0) = 3, therefore, a = 3
The relationship is $y = 3e^{-1.2x}$

BAR GRAPHS

Bar graphs are used to represent numerical information when
the objective is to compare groups of data or variables. The
bars may be horizontal or vertical, see Figure 13.5. It is much
easier to construct using an electronic spreadsheet. However,

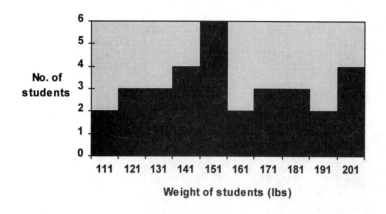

(a)

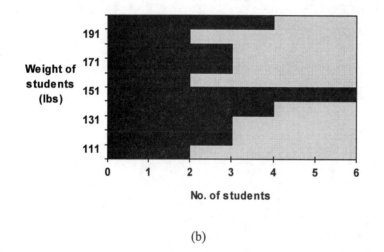

(b)

Figure 13.5   Typical bar graph: (a) vertical   (b) horizontal

the construction of bar graphs is simple. First, lay off the horizontal and vertical axes in such a way that they fit the given data. Then construct each vertical bar making sure that the spacing between each bar is less than the width of the bars.

PIE GRAPHS

Pie graphs are used to compare the relationship of parts or the percentage to a whole. A typical pie graph is shown in Figure 13.6. It is best used when there are not many parts. Its construction involves the division of a circle into sectors. Each vector is obtained by multiplying the fraction or percentage of the part to the whole by 360°. For example, if the part is 10% of the whole, then it should be represented as a sector with an included angle of 36°. It is important to label the percentage or fraction of each part on the pie chart as well as the variables the chart represents.

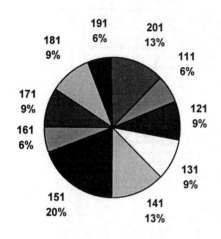

Figure 13.6. A typical Pie graph

13.3 TECHNICAL SKETCHING

Technical sketching is the process of communicating in a rapid and effective manner a design concept, idea or main features of a product. For the most part, it involves free hand drawing of the parts. Advances in the CAD systems have made it possible to sketch through the use of a computer.

Sketching is an important skill that a designer must develop because the conceptual design phase requires that the various alternatives be represented in forms that can be easily understood. Sketching is a skill that can be acquired by constant practice and patience. It requires a lot of time to be proficient in the art of technical sketching. However, if you want to be an effective designer who can convey design ideas quickly, you must develop this skill.

If sketching is done by free hand, the only tools you need are pencils with soft leads, preferable an H or 2H, an eraser and paper. The paper size should preferably be 8½" x 11" with grids. The two most common used papers with grids are the square **grid** and **isometric**, see Figure 13.7

There are certain principles that should be adhered to which

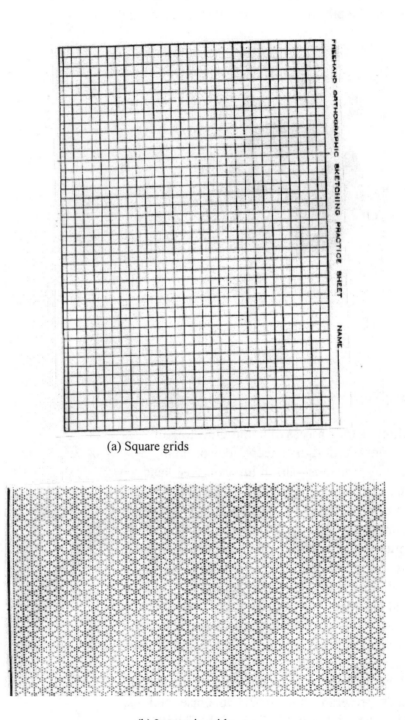

(a) Square grids

(b) Isometric grids

Figure 13.7 Freehand sketching papers

will make sketching a little easier. Since straight lines and curved lines are difficult to produce without the aid of grids, it is suggested, if it is all possible, to do the sketching on grid paper. Lines can be drawn straighter if you rest your arm on a firm support. If the line is too long you may consider changing the orientation of the paper as often as it is necessary and using a series of connected short lines. The implication of this is that the paper should not be attached to any drawing board or surface. During sketching the pencil should be gripped as firmly as possible while relaxing the arm and the rest of the body. In addition, you should maintain a comfortable angle for sketching.

SKETCHING ARCS AND CIRCLES

Because many products can be sketched with lines, arcs and circles and since it is difficult to sketch arcs and circles, the steps involved shown in Figure 13.8 are as follows:

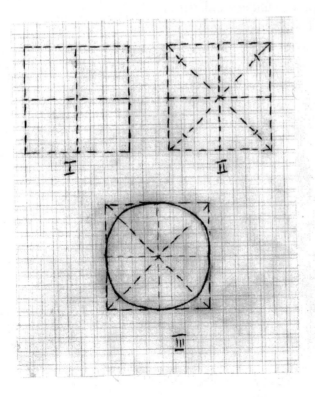

Figure 13.8 Steps involved in sketching an
arc or a circle

Step 1. Lightly draw a square with sides equal to the diameter of the circle or arc to be sketched. Note that a paper with grids is most useful. Mark the mid points of the sides of the square. Using the mid points sketch vertical and horizontal lines. Their point of intersection is the center of the circle.

Step 2. Join the diagonals of the square using faint lines. Beginning from the center mark off distances, along the diagonals, equal to the radius of the circle. Each distance is approximately two-thirds of the distance, along the diagonal, from the center. The layout now consists of eight marks.

Step 3. Sketch short arcs from one mark off point to another rotating the paper as you draw the arcs. Continue the process until the circle has been completed or the appropriate arc has been drawn. Then overdraw the arcs with thick dark more continuous lines to obtain the desired circle or arc.

ISOMETRIC SKETCHING

Communication of any kind loses its meaning when what is communicated is difficult to interpret or understand. In engineering design, one of the best ways to communicate design ideas is the use of pictorial representation. Pictorial representations can be in the form of **axonometric**, **oblique** or **perspective** projections. Technical sketching of pictorials commonly involves isometric drawings which is a form of axonometric pictorial. Consequently, only the isometric sketching is discussed here.

Isometric sketching is best done using the isometric grid paper. However, since this may not be readily available to you when it is needed, the more general principles are presented. Sketching requires the use of isometric axes. These consist of a vertical line and two lines that are drawn thirty degrees from the horizontal on either side of the vertical line (see Figure 13.9). Using these axes a construction box is sketched making

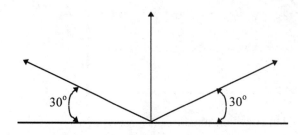

Figure 13.9 Axes for isometric sketching

sure that each edge of the box is parallel to the defined new axes. An object can then be sketched. It is important to realize that any dimensions on isometric axes are true measurements. Any dimension not on these axes is not to be considered a true dimension. Details can be added using the construction box to represent the object that is to be sketched. It must be noted that if there is a hole, it is sketched as an ellipse. An ellipse can be sketched following the same procedure used in sketching circles. The only difference is that the axes used are parallel to the isometric axes.

13.4 WORKING AND ASSEMBLY DRAWINGS

The final communication of a design is usually done through what is known as working drawings or production drawings. On the other hand, the manner in which each component of the product is put together to form the final product is shown by an **assembly drawing.**

The working drawings, also known as **detail drawings**, contain the necessary information relevant to the manufacture of parts. Such information includes shapes, dimensions and tolerances, materials, type of finish and specifications. A typical working drawing is shown in Figure 13.10.

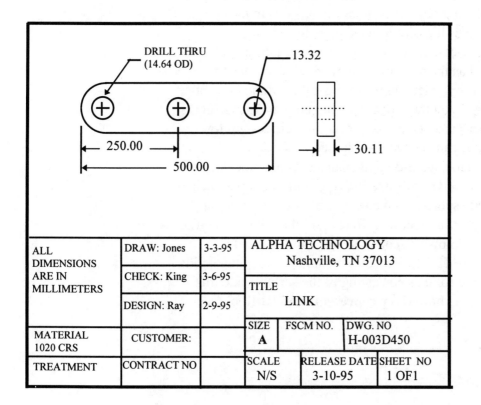

ALL DIMENSIONS ARE IN MILLIMETERS	DRAW: Jones	3-3-95	ALPHA TECHNOLOGY Nashville, TN 37013			
	CHECK: King	3-6-95	TITLE			
	DESIGN: Ray	2-9-95	LINK			
MATERIAL 1020 CRS	CUSTOMER:		SIZE A	FSCM NO.	DWG. NO H-003D450	
TREATMENT	CONTRACT NO		SCALE N/S	RELEASE DATE 3-10-95	SHEET NO 1 OF1	

Figure 13.10 Sample detail drawing

The assembly drawings do not need the detailed information given in the detailed drawings because they serve as a guide to how the parts fit together. The most important thing in an assembly drawing is to communicate clearly how the parts fit together. An assembly drawing may be either an orthographic or pictorial drawing. Of course, there is no doubt that a pictorial assembly drawing is preferred to the orthographic assembly drawing. When using the pictorial drawing, center lines are often used to show how the parts are assembled. Since the assembly drawings contain all the parts of the product, each part is assigned a number or a letter with descriptions of the parts and the number of each part required in the assembly (see Figure 13.11).

13.5 GEOMETRIC MODELING

Geometric modeling is concerned mostly with how to describe a three-dimensional, continuous object in a finite and discrete digital computer. The representation of three-dimensional objects have been accomplished by the use of either wireframe or solid model. There are advantages to actually representing objects in three-dimensions in the computer. It makes it easier for designers to simulate manufacturing processes. For example, a hole through a solid may be modeled as the removal of a cylinder from the object. The radius of the cylinder should be the radius of the ball cutter that may be used. Another advantage of geometric modeling is that some properties that engineers need in their design, for example, volume, can easily be computed.

In CAD systems, three-dimensional solids are modeled by representing the solid as a collection of primitive shapes such as blocks, cylinders, spheres, and cones. The solid is obtained either by adding or subtracting different solids. This method of building solids is known as **constructive solid geometry** (CSG), (see Figure 13.12). Another method of modeling solids is to represent the solid as consisting of the surfaces and this method is known as **boundary representation** (B-Rep) (see Figure 13.13).

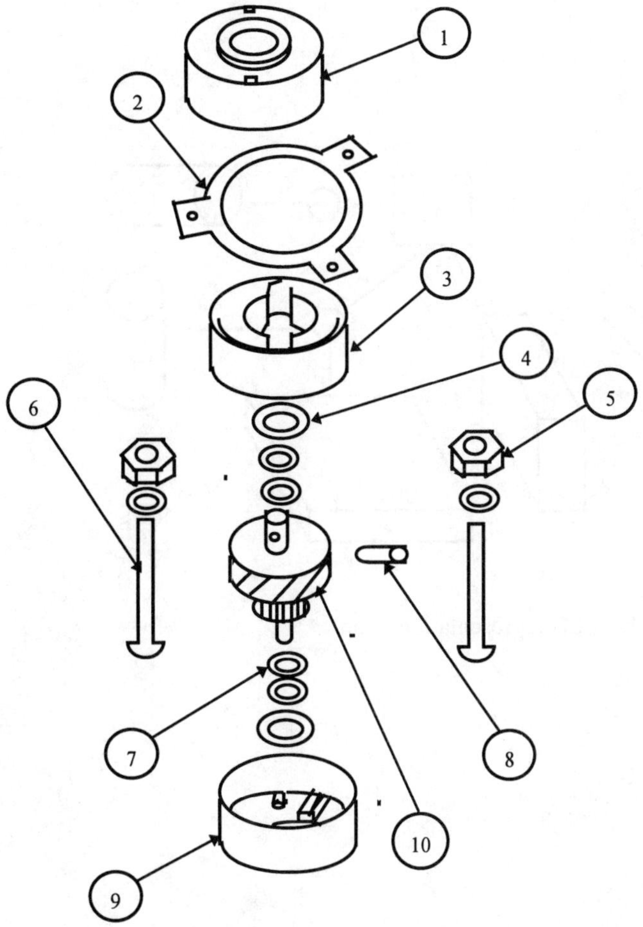

ITEM NO.	DESCRIPTION	PART NO.	
1	END CAP ASSEMBLY		
2	MOUNTING BRACKET		
3	FLUX RING SUBASSEMBLY		
4	OIL THROW WASHER		
5	NUT		
6	BOLT		
7	NYLATRON WASHERS		
8	ROLL PIN		
9	END CAP		
10	ARMATURE		

PART LIST

	DRAWN : JONES	3-3-95	ALPHA TECHNOLOGY Nashville, TN 37013		
	CHECK: KING	3-6-95	TITLE : ASSEMBLY ELECTRIC MOTOR		
	DESIGN: RAY	2-9-95			
TREATMENT	CONTRACT NO.		SIZE	FSCM NO DWG.NO A036	
MATERIAL	CUSTOMER		SCALE	RELEASE DATE	SHEET

Figure 13.11 Sample Assembly Drawing

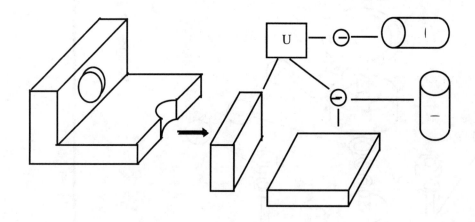

Figure 13.12 CSG representation of an object

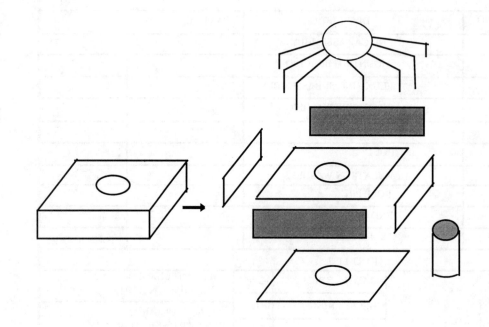

Figure 13.13. B-rep of an object

Many CAD software packages such as AUTOCAD and CADKEY have commands that allow you to build solids and surfaces. It is important, therefore, that you master how to use these tools as they are very essential in today's engineering or design practices. With respect to paperless industry, CAD systems help in this concept. You can create objects, various kinds of drawings, prepare manufacturing information and send them to the manufacturing unit without ever printing them. The point is that it is important that you become proficient in the area of geometric modeling because of its importance in engineering practice.

PROBLEMS

13.1 Use a graphical approach to find the equation that
describes the data given below

x	0.30	0.40	0.60	0.70	0.80	1.00	1.10	1.20	1.30	1.40
y	0.71	0.58	0.39	0.32	0.26	0.18	0.14	1.12	0.10	0.08

13.2 Repeat problem 13.1 using a different graph paper.

13.3 Practice sketching arcs and circles of different radii.

13.4 Using isometric grid paper practice sketching various
objects such as a nail clipper and the mouse that is on one
of the computers in your school.

SECTION THREE

DESIGN FOR MANUFACTURABILITY

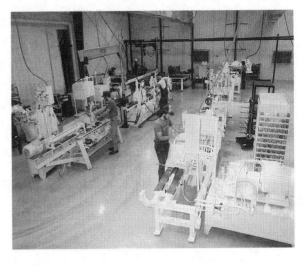

INTRODUCTION TO SECTION THREE

A manufacturing plant
*Courtesy of Hol-Mac Corporation,
Bay Springs, MS.*

In the past few decades engineers as designers have ignored the importance of manufacturing in the design process. They paid little attention to how the products they designed were to be manufactured. This has not always been the case. For example, the pioneers of the automobile industry, which included such men as Henry Ford and Ransom Olds, were not only designers but they were process engineers who understood how their products were manufactured.

Recently there is a renewed interest in having engineers understand how things are manufactured. This interest has been labeled different names such as **concurrent engineering** and **simultaneous engineering**. It does not matter what terminology is used; the concept is the same. The underlying concept is that the design, the manufacture, the sales and the disposal of a product must be viewed as an integrated process. Another way of looking at this is that a product design team must at least include design engineers, manufacturing engineers and sales persons. The purpose of this section is to raise awareness in the engineering student of the other essential factors that must be considered during a design process. Manufacturing involves at least two factors- transformation of raw materials into desired parts and the assembly of various elements that make up the products. Therefore, Chapter 14 introduces the student to some basic concepts in materials and manufacturing processes and Chapter 15 addresses some issues of assembly in the design stage.

NOTES

CHAPTER 14

MATERIALS AND MANUFACTURING PROCESSES

14.1 INTRODUCTION

The desire for high quality inexpensive products means that the designer or modern engineer must be concerned not only with the functionality of the product but also with the manufacture of the product. This means that the designer must know something about the material that is to be used in the design. In addition, there must be a fundamental knowledge of how the product is to be manufactured. These requirements demand basic knowledge in material science and various manufacturing processes. This basic knowledge will help the design engineer to realize that there is an interrelationship between the form, the materials and the manufacturing methods of any desired product. Furthermore, without this knowledge the designer is limited in material selection for the designed product. The goal of this chapter is to introduce the student to the importance of manufacturing processes in the design phase of a product. Several texts have been written in these areas and the reader will soon take courses that will give an in-depth knowledge of these topics. Therefore, what is intended here is to provide some concepts and terminology with which the engineering student must become familiar in order to become a good designer in today's industry.

14.2 MATERIALS SCIENCE

It is important to understand the behavior of materials that are used in the design. Material science *is concerned with the study of the relationships that exist between the internal structures and properties of materials*. The term "structure" means the internal arrangement of atoms and molecules relative to each other.

In order for the designer to specify a particular material for a designed product the properties required of the part must be decided. This is because material selection is based on properties such as: **chemical**, **physical** and **mechanical** properties.

MATERIAL PROPERTIES AND SELECTION

A material characteristic that relates to the structure of the material is known as the **chemical property**. Chemical properties involve such things as the chemical composition of the material or corrosion resistance (ability to resist deterioration by chemical reaction). In selecting any material for design, the designer must make every effort to determine what the material is made of, otherwise it is possible either to select the wrong material or even to select a very costly material when a cheaper material will suffice. One situation that a designer may be concerned with is that of corrosion resistance when a product is to be subjected to a hostile environment. For example, products for off-shore drilling that come in contact with salt water must be designed with materials that are rust resistant.

Physical properties are the characteristics necessary to describe the interaction between materials and various forms of energy as well as with other forms of matter. Physical properties include **density, melting point, thermal expansion** (the rate at which materials change in dimension as a result of change in temperature), and **thermal conductivity** (the rate of heat flow through a material per unit area per unit time as a result of temperature change). In selecting a material for design application where extreme temperatures are encountered, the designer must pay close attention to the thermal conductivity and thermal expansion. Another situation where thermal expansion may be of great importance is when dissimilar materials that are fastened together are to be heated. If weight is a major concern in the product, the designer must then be concerned with the density of the material to be selected.

Mechanical properties are those characteristics of materials that are useful in describing the behavior of materials when they are subjected to forces, see Figure 14.1. They normally relate to the elastic or inelastic behavior of the material. A material is elastic if it deforms under a load but returns to its original condition when the load is removed. Some mechanical properties include **yield strength, hardness** and **modulus of elasticity**. Yield strength is the stress at which materials deviate from the linear relationship between stress and strain. Hardness is a measure of the resistance of metal to permanent(plastic) deformation. Modulus of elasticity is a measure of the rigidity or stiffness of the material. Another property that may be of

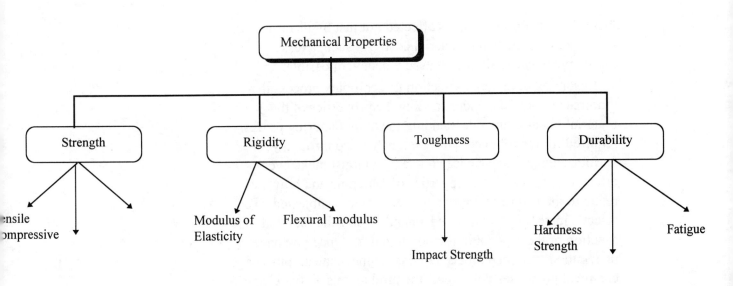

Figure 14.1 Typical mechanical properties considered in
the design of structural elements

importance to an engineer who is concerned with a product
sustaining impact load is **toughness** (a measure of the amount
of energy which a material can absorb before fracturing). It
becomes important that the designer understands these
properties as they relate to the product design. If load carrying
ability, under static condition, is of concern the yield strength of
material to be selected must be carefully investigated. Hardness
affects the machinability of a metal. This must be taken into
consideration in selecting material to be specified for a designed
product.

It cannot be over-emphasized that products are made of
materials. Although the designer must not necessarily be a
material scientist or metallurgist, he must have the basic
knowledge of materials to make intelligent decisions or at least
be able to ask the right kind of questions to the material scientist
and metallurgist. Because there are several material properties
that can be considered, it is vital that the designer considers only
those that are essential to the function of the part or product to
be designed.

There are at least two other factors that must be considered
during the material selection process. The first is the
availability of the material. It does not make sense to select a
material that is not readily available or that can cause delay in
product development because of the time involved in acquiring
the material. In such cases, designers must use sound judgment
in selecting alternative easily obtainable materials. The second

factor is cost. Product cost is affected not just by its design or manufacturing costs but material cost. As such, a less expensive material should be used whenever possible.

In summary, material selection is a complex process that requires not only the understanding the properties of the material but also an understanding the manufacturing processes required for the product. However, as you go through your various engineering science courses, you must make every effort to understand the properties of materials and how they relate to the nature of loads to which they are subjected. To select a material you must understand clearly the required function of the product in relation to loads. Once you have understood that, then proceed to list the mechanical, physical or chemical properties you expect the product to satisfy. Using this you may select tentatively, the material for the design of the product. The term "tentative" is used because final material selection is also affected by the manufacturing process of the product. For example, a designer, who has selected a harder material, may realize that considering the difficulty in machining the part, an alternative softer material should be chosen.

14.3 MANUFACTURING PROCESSES

Material selection and manufacturing process selection go hand in hand. A manufacturing process is concerned with the conversion of raw or unfinished material to a finished or final product using tools and machines. There are many processes that are utilized to obtain the desired shape of any manufactured product or component, see Figure 14.2. These processes may involve the changing of shape of a raw material stock without either taking material from it or adding material to it. Or it could involve removing parts of the material stock to obtain the desired shape. It could also involve joining two parts together to obtain the desired shape. These processes can broadly be categorized as unique processes that are briefly discussed below.

Machining

Machining involves material removal using processes such as cutting, drilling, boring, grinding, etc. Machining may be preferred to other methods of producing a part when great dimensional accuracy is required. Some surface characteristics

Drilling Operation
Courtesy of Hol-Mac Corp

or finishes are better obtained by machining operations than by any

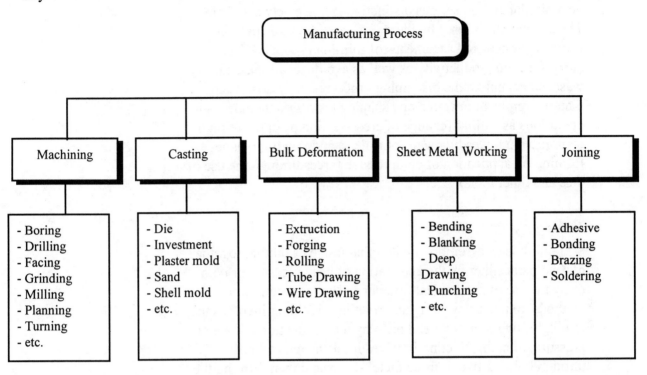

Figure 14.2 Typical manufacturing processes

other processes. Of course, there are disadvantages to machining. For example, it takes longer to remove materials from a work piece to obtain the desired shape or form than some of the other processes.

Casting

Casting is one of the oldest processes for forming shapes. Metallic casting involves melting a metal and pouring it into a mold cavity of the same shape as that of the desired product shape. Engine blocks are generally produced by this method. In addition, this method is economical. It is the favored process when complex shapes with hollow sections are required and when large parts are to be produced.

Forming and Shaping

The forming and shaping processes are used to change the shape of objects. Forming processes usually involve the application of compressive forces. Shaping, on the other hand, usually involves molding and casting. The two processes are very similar and no serious distinction is made between them. The advantages offered by these processes cause them to be seriously considered as a means of forming products. They allow for high productivity as well as avoidance of material waste since, unlike the machining processes, they do not require material removal. Forming and shaping processes include such operations as **rolling** (change of cross-section by application of compressive forces by means of rollers) and **forging** (shape forming by application of compressive forces through the use of dies and other tools).

Joining

Joining is an assembly method that involves putting together of two parts either by the application of heat, pressure or both or by the use of mechanical fasteners. The most common methods in use are welding and riveting. Welding involves the joining of two or more metal parts by the application of heat or pressure, or both. Riveting involves inserting a metal pin through holes in two or more metal sheets and then forming the ends of the pin usually called heads.

Joining process should be considered during the design process especially if it is impossible to manufacture a part as a single system or when it is more economical and easier to manufacture the product as single components which are then assembled. Another situation in which joining may be considered involves huge structures which are fabricated at a manufacturing plant but are to be used at different locations to form more complex structures. This is the case in the building/construction industry. Further discussion of joining process is presented in the next chapter.

PROCESS SELECTION

Process selection is guided by several factors. Some of the important factors considered are part size, shape capability and production volume. For example, if the material specified is steel and the part size is less than 800 mm and the shape is of moderate complexity with no internal undercuts and the production volume is less than 10,000 units, the forging process may be selected. To make the best possible choice of the process for a given product, it is equally important that the quality of the finished product be taken into consideration as well as the cost-effectiveness of the selected process.

SOURCES USED

DeGarmo, E.P., Black, J.T., and Kosher, R.A., **Materials and Processes in Manufacturing**, 7th edition, Macmillan Publishing Company, New York, 1988.

Kalpakjian, S., **Manufacturing Engineering and Technology**, Third Edition, Addison-Wesley Publishing Company, New York, 1995.

Smith, W.F., **Principles of Materials Science and Engineering**, McGraw-Hill Inc., New York, 1996.

PROBLEMS

14.1 Why should a machinist be concerned about the hardness of a material?

14.2 State two factors that must be considered in selection of materials for design.

14.3 Interview a professor in your university who teaches materials science to find out why this subject should be of a concern to you in your chosen discipline. Summary your findings.

14.4 Visit two local manufacturing plants and observe what is involved in manufacturing a part. Write in detail describing what what machining operations you observed.

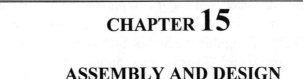

CHAPTER 15

ASSEMBLY AND DESIGN

15.1 INTRODUCTION

An important activity of the manufacturing process is the assembly of the various machined parts to form the desired product. This process, whether performed manually or automatically, can be expensive and time consuming. Assembly problems encountered may be due to exceeding the specified limits of tolerance causing difficulties in putting components together. Also, deficient processing of parts can cause difficulties during the assembly process. Therefore, to avoid undue problems during assembly the engineer must consider how the components are to be put together in the design phase of the product development. The designer must not only be concerned with satisfying the functionality of the parts but also with the materials for the components, and finally with the assembly method.

The purpose of this chapter to introduce the student to some of the assembly processes and the rules that must be mastered in order to be assembly conscious during the design phase.

15.2 ASSEMBLY PROCESS

The main function of an assembly is to join components. The joining of components is achieved by means of form, force, and material. Assembly by means of form may involve changing the shape of components. This may involve rolling as described in the previous chapter or it may involve simple bending operations. Joining by means of force may involve forcing one part into another of slightly smaller dimension, or it could be by use of screws or rivets. Joining by material involves such operations as welding, soldering and gluing. Joining can be strictly viewed as an assembly process. However it can be treated as a manufacturing process. The fact that joining is not simply an assembly process supports the notion that an assembly process is a subset of the manufacturing process.

Welding or soldering is used when it is desired to permanently join two parts together. If a product needs to be disassembled for maintenance, welding is not a good choice.

Welding operation
Courtesy of Hol-Mac Corp

Even when welding is an acceptable form of assembly, the location and accessibility of two parts to be welded in the product must be considered. Of course, another factor to consider in using this method is not just the cost but the appearance issue. If aesthetics is an important consideration, the parts must be designed to avoid the use of welds if it is at all possible.

Riveting is also used to form a permanent joint. It has the added advantage that it can be used to join together parts made of disparate materials. However, the designer must avoid placing the rivets too close to the edge of the parts that are to be riveted together to avoid the problem of tearing of the parts when subjected to external loads.

Assembly methods that involve the use of force include shrink and press fits. Shrink fit makes use of the fact that two parts to be shrink fitted have different thermal expansion and contraction. Press fit involves forcing one component of a bigger dimension into another component of smaller dimension.

Regardless of the means by which components are joined together, the assembly process involves three major operations: **handling**, **composing** and **checking**. Handling implies that in designing the parts the designer must consider such issues as transportation of the parts from one location to another either manually or by the use of conveyor systems. In addition, since parts must be positioned or aligned before being inserted into another part, the designer must consider this in designing the parts for assembly. Composing deals with forming permanent connections between parts. Checking is a process by which the assembly operator ensures that the components are properly positioned or assembled in the right sequence. Perhaps of greatest concern to the designer is the issue of handling regardless of how parts are to be assembled: manually or by an automated procedure. This is not to say that the designer must overlook the composing processes but rather that great emphasis must be given to the question of handling. Parts that are poorly designed can cause other handling problems such as tangling or jamming of the conveyor systems.

15.3 ASSEMBLY SYSTEMS

The cost of assembly of any product is also related to the method involved in its assembly. Therefore, a design engineer must consider the assembly systems during the design phase. An assembly system consists of an operator or an assembler and assembly tools. The assembly tools may be simply hand held tools such as a wrench or it could be as complex as a robot system.

In broad terms the assembly system falls into three categories: manual, semi-automatic, and automatic. Manual assembly is carried out using simple equipment consisting of hand tools, fixtures and tables. A semi-automatic assembly system means that some part of the assembly task is performed manually while others are performed using programmed machines. An automated system performs the assembly task by following computer programs. It is able to perform its task by using the input information supplied by the programmer.

From the above considerations, it is clear that an assembly system requires assembly equipment, transportation equipment and a means of storage. The assembly equipment includes the manual work area with fixtures, hand tools, measuring devices and boxes for parts and components. For semi-automatic or fully automatic systems, assembly machines are also required. Transportation equipment includes the conveyor systems and other means of carrying the parts from machining stations to assembly stations.

The understanding of the assembly system is very essential for at least two reasons. First, it aids the designer at the design phase to make the right choice regarding the assembly method to be used for the product. Second, it makes it easier for the designer to realize that while certain assembly operations may be very easy for the manual method, such an operation may be impossible for an automated system. This helps in design decisions that are not costly to fix at the assembly stage.

15.4 DESIGN FOR ASSEMBLY PRINCIPLES

Design for Assembly (DFA) is a methodology aimed at improving product design to minimize assembly cost by making components more tractable to both manual and automatic assembly processes. This methodology is important because correct application of it has led to reduction of assembly time and consequently increase in productivity of many companies such as IBM and Xerox.

Design for Assembly is guided by certain overall principles. The most fundamental principle is to reduce the number of parts in a system whenever possible. Another important principle is to design products and components to be suitable for uni-directional assembly. Miles [1989] has given fourteen principles that govern this design philosophy. These principles are broad based and not specific as to be helpful to the designer.

It is for this purpose that some design rules have to be developed.

RULES FOR DESIGN FOR ASSEMBLY

In an effort to provide more precise guidelines, several rules have been developed for DFA. The rules are not ranked and therefore no one rule is considered more important than the other. The ones listed are primarily due to Boothroyd and Dewhurst [1983] and Hoekstra [1989].

Rule 1: Design for easy grip of components. Desirable features include flat surfaces, holes, slots, and tabs. Compare Fig 15.1a and b.

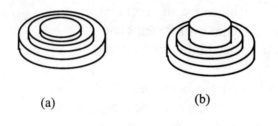

(a)   (b)

Figure 15.1 (a) Part unsuitable to grip
(b) Part adaptable to grip

Rule 2: Avoid using fasteners whenever possible. If it is not possible, then reduce their number or use the same fasteners throughout the assembly. It is preferable to use integral fasteners instead of separate fasteners (compare Figure 15.2a and b). There are at least three reasons to avoid the use of

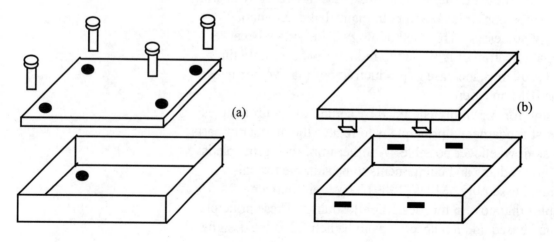

Figure 15.2 (a) Part with screws
(b) Part redesigned with integral fasteners instead of separate ones

fasteners. First, their use may require the assembling of the fasteners themselves especially when using bolts and washers. Second, the application of torque to fasteners must be done carefully to avoid failures of the assembled parts as a result of failure of the fasteners due to unsatisfactory pre-load. Third, assembling with fasteners may prove difficult or impossible for automatic assembly.

Rule 3: Design parts to avoid tangling or nesting of components. This is prevented by using parts with features that cannot be hooked into another part. If springs are to be used their ends should be closed (see Figure 15. 3a and b).

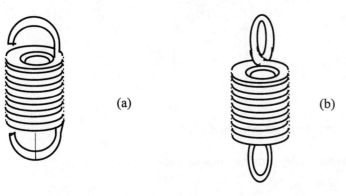

(a)   (b)

Figure 15.3   (a) Open end spring: may cause nesting
              (b) Closed end spring: preferred for assembly

Rule 4: Design parts to have location points that make it impossible for the parts to be incorrectly assembled (see Figure 15.4).

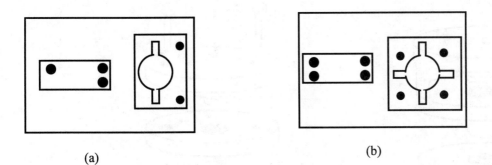

(a)   (b)

Figure 15.4   (a) Parts may be wrongly assembled because of incorrect orientation
              (b) Part cannot be incorrectly assembled because of symmetry, there
                  is no problem with orientation

Rule 5: Parts should be designed for easy insertion. Therefore, both internal and external chamfers should be used (see Figure 15.5).

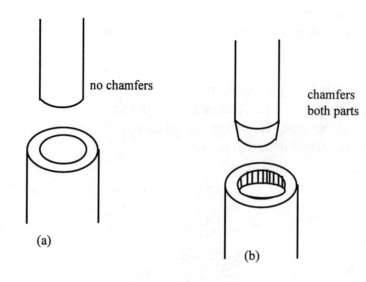

Figure 15.5 (a) Part may be difficult to assemble due to absence of
chamfers.
(b) Chamfers make the two mating parts easy to assemble

Rule 6: Design parts for uni-directional assembly especially if the mode of assembly is by insertion (see Figure 15.6). An alternate rule is that the product should be designed for stacking. This means that the components are laid on top of each other during the assembly of the product.

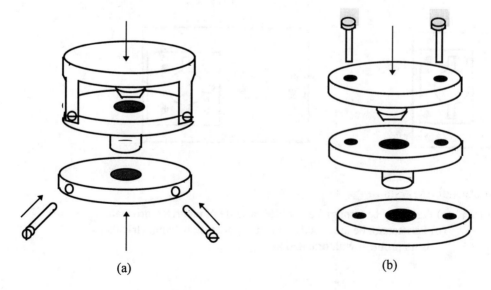

Figure 15.6 (a) Assembly involves too many directions
(b) Assembly involves only one direction, therefore preferred.

Rule 7: Avoid the use of flexible parts as they may cause tangling of parts during transportation of parts from machining station to assembly station (see Figure 15.7).

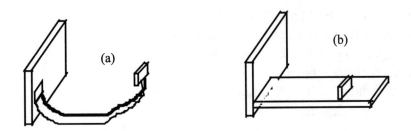

Figure 15.7 (a) Part has a flexible component that may cause tangling.
(b) Part has no flexible component, therefore good for assembly

APPLYING DESIGN FOR ASSEMBLY PRINCIPLES

It is important to realize that an important implication of the rules stated above is that it is desirable to avoid assembly altogether in order not to incur assembly cost. This means that components must be integrated. Three questions must be answered to help decide whether to integrate parts. The first is: does one part move relative to another? The second is: can the two parts to be integrated be made of the same material? The third is: how does integration affect production and assembly costs? If the answers to these three questions are in the affirmative, the parts should be integrated. The detailed analysis involved in applying the DFA method is beyond the scope of this book but the general approach as outlined in Lucas DFA procedure in Miles (89), with some modifications, is summarized below.

Step 1
   Use block diagrams to describe the various operations involved in the assembling of the product proposed in the conceptual phase of the design.

Step 2
   Perform functional analysis of each component to see if its function is necessary for the performance of the product. The components whose function are simply fastening or locating should be considered as targets of elimination or redesign.

Step 3

Carry out a fitting analysis. Examine the ease with which each part can be handled both for transportation to the assembly station and for assembly itself. Normally, a value is assigned to each component based on this criteria. Next, using the diagram of step 1, an insertion process analysis is performed. The objective is to identify the fitting processes that are very expensive. Again a subjective index is assigned to each fitting process and those with high values are considered as candidates for redesign.

Step 4

Conduct a feeding analysis. The objective is to determine components that will cause difficulty during their transportation to the final assembly station. Those identified are candidates for redesign.

At the end of the analysis, the designer returns to the conceptual phase to incorporate some of the modifications suggested by DFA analysis. This may result in either eliminating some unnecessary parts or at least simplifying the assembly process.

Example 15.1

Consider the subassembly, Figure 15.8a, consisting of three components. The principles of DFA can be applied to obtain Figure 15.8b. Asking the question " Can the three parts be made of the same material?" The answer is yes. Of course, there are more rigorous analyses that are often performed. But this example is meant to shown that even without rigorous analysis the principles of DFA can be applied to minimize the number of parts in a system. ,

Bolt   Washer   Spacer

(a)

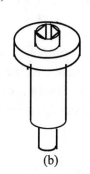

(b)

Figure 15.8 (a) Three parts - bolt, washer and spacer
(b) One part - cold-headed fastener

SOURCES USED

Andreasen, M.M., S. Khler, and T. Lund **Design for Assembly**, Second Edition, IFS Publications, UK, Springer-Verlag, New York, 1988.

Boothroyd, G. and Dewhurst, P. **Design for Assembly - A Designer's Handbook**, Department of Mechanical Engineering. University of Massachusetts, Amhurst, 1983

Boothroyd, G., Poli, C., and Murch, L.E., **The Handbook of Feeding and Orienting Techniques for Small Parts**, Department of Mechanical Engineering, University of Massachusetts, Amherst, Mass., 1977.

Budinski, K., **Engineering Materials - Properties & Selection**, Third Edition, Prentice Hall, Englewood Cliffs, New Jersey, 1989.

ElWakil S.D., **Processes and Design For Manufacturing**, Prentice Hall, Englewood Cliffs, New Jersey, 1989.

Hoekstra "Design for Automated Assembly : An Axiomatic and Analytical Method", SME Technical Paper, AD89-416, presented at the SME International Conference, Detroit, Michigan, May 1-4, 1989.

Kalpakjian, S., **Manufacturing Engineering and Technology**, Third Edition, Addison-Wesley Publishing Company, Reading, MA., 1995.

Onwubiko, C. and G. Bekey, "Group Technology for DFA: An Intermediate Step for DFA Advisory Systems," **Journal of Applied Manufacturing Systems**, Vol. 5, No.1, Fall 1992, pp. 59-67.

PROBLEMS

15.1 The three pieces shown in Fig.P15.1 are to be assembled
as shown. What do you see a potential problem (s) in the
assembly of the parts. Redesign the parts to remove the
problem (s) you identified.

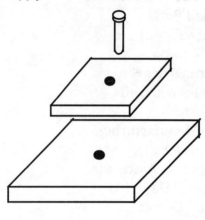

Fig .P15.1

15.2 The sub assembly shown in Fig.P15.2 is considered poor
in terms of design for assembly.   Give at least two
reasons for this assessment. Suggest how you will
redesign the components to be better suited for easy
assembly.

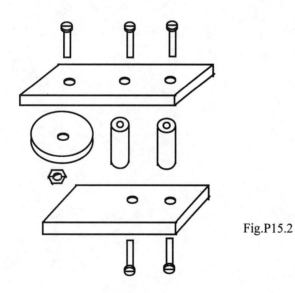

Fig.P15.2

15.3 The circuit board shown in Fig.P15.3 is to be analyzed for design for assembly. Identify what could cause problems in mass assembly. Sketch a redesigned assembly.

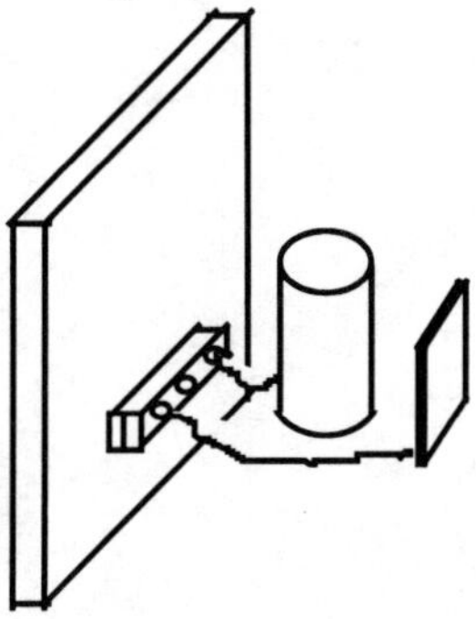

Fig.P15.3

NOTES

APPENDIX A - UNIT CONVERSIONS

To convert from	To	Multiply by
acres	ft^2	4.356 x 10^4
acres	m^2	4.046 9 x 10^3
amperes	C/s	1
ampere hours	C	3.6 x 10^3
atmospheres	lbf/in^2	1.469 6 x 10^1
atmospheres	Pa	1.01 33 x 10^5
barrels (US)	gal (US liquid)	4.2 x 10^1
bars	lbf/in^2	1.450 4 x 10^1
bars	Pa	1 x 10^5
Btu	ft lbf	7.776 5 x 10^2
Btu	hp h	3.927 5 x 10^{-4}
Btu	J	1.055 1 x 10^3
Btu /hr	ft lbf/s	2.160 1 x 10^{-1}
Btu/hr	hp	3.927 5 x 10^{-4}
Bushels (US)	ft^3	1.244 5
Bushels (US)	m^3	3.523 9 x 10^{-2}
centimeters	in	3.937 0 x 10^{-1}
cubic centimeters	in^3	6.102 4 x 10^{-2}
cubic centimeters	L	1 x 10^{-3}
cubic centimeters	oz (US fluid)	3.381 x 10^{-2}
cubic centimeters per second	ft^3/min	2.118 9 x 10^{-3}
cubic centimeters per second	gal (US liquid)/min	1.585 0 x 10^{-2}
cubic feet	gal (US liquid)	7.480 5
cubic feet	in^3	1.728 x 10^3
cubic feet	L	2.8317 x 10^1
cubic feet per minute	L/s	4.719 5 x 10^{-1}
cubic meters	ft^3	3.531 5 x 10^1
cubic meters	L	1 x 10^3
feet	m	3.048 x 10^{-1}
feet	mi	1.893 9 x 10^{-4}
foot pound-force	J	1.355 8
horsepower	W	7.457 0 x 10^2
gallon	L	3.785 4
grams	lbm	2.204 6 x 10^{-3}
joules	kWh	2.777 8 x 10^{-7}
pounds-force	N	4.448 2
pounds-mass	kg	4.535 9 x 10^{-1}
pound -force per square inches	Pa	6.894 8 x 10^3
pounds-mass per cubic foot	kg/m^3	1.6018 x 10^1
radians	r (revolutions)	1.5915 x 10^{-1}
radians per second	r/min	9.549 3
slugs	lbm	3.217 4 x 10^1
slugs	kg	1.459 4 x 10^1
square centimeters	ft^2	1.0764 x 10^{-3}
square feet	m^2	9.290 3 x 10^{-2}
square miles	km^2	2.590 0
tons (long)	lbm	2.24 x 10^3

APPENDIX B - TRIGONOMETRY REVIEW

Introduction

This appendix is for quick review of trigonometry. It is not intended to be a comprehensive treatment of the subject rather a brief review of this important subject.

Angles and Trigonometric Functions

The two most commonly used measure of angles in engineering applications are- **degrees** and **radians**. A degree is 1/360 of the central angle of a circle. A radian is the angle subtended at the center of a circle by an arc equal to the radius .

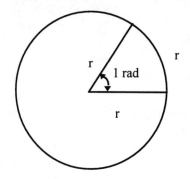

The relationship between the two is as follows:

$$180^\circ = \pi \text{ radians}$$

The trigonometric functions are defined with reference to a right angle triangle.

$$\sin \theta = \frac{opposite\ side}{hypotenuse} = \frac{b}{c}$$

$$\cos \theta = \frac{adjacent\ side}{hypotenuse} = \frac{a}{c}$$

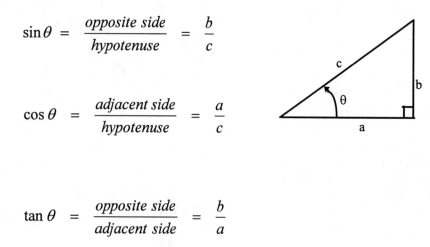

$$\tan \theta = \frac{opposite\ side}{adjacent\ side} = \frac{b}{a}$$

$$\cot \theta = \frac{1}{\tan \theta} = \frac{adjacent\ side}{opposite\ side} = \frac{a}{b}$$

$$\sec \theta = \frac{1}{\cos \theta} = \frac{hypotenuse}{adjacent \ side} = \frac{c}{a}$$

$$\csc \theta = \frac{1}{\sin \theta} = \frac{hypotenuse}{opposite \ side} = \frac{c}{b}$$

When θ is the argument of a trigonometric function, the sign of the value of the function depends on the quadrant on which it is located. The sign is positive for all the functions when θ is in the first quadrant. The acronym CAST written from the fourth quadrant is useful in remembering this relation. This means Cosine, All , Sine and Tangent are positive in the indicated quadrant.

Only sin is positive	All trig. functions are positive	S- sin	A - all
Only tan is positive	Only cos is positive	T- tan	C - cos

Identities and Relationships

$$\sin^2 \theta + \cos^2 \theta = 1$$

$$\tan^2 \theta + 1 = \sec^2 \theta$$

$$1 + \cot^2 \theta = \csc^2 \theta$$

$$\sin \theta = \cos(90^\circ - \theta) = \sin (180^\circ - \theta)$$

$$\cos \theta = \sin (90^\circ - \theta) = -\cos (180^\circ - \theta)$$

$$\tan \theta = \cot (90^\circ - \theta) = - \tan(180^\circ - \theta)$$

$$\sin (-\theta) = - \sin \theta$$

$$\cos (-\theta) = \cos \theta$$

Summation formulas

$$\sin(\theta \pm \beta) = \sin\theta \cos\beta \pm \cos\theta \sin\beta$$

$$\cos(\theta \pm \beta) = \cos\theta \cos\beta \mp \sin\theta \sin\beta$$

$$\tan(\theta \pm \beta) = \frac{\tan\theta \pm \tan\beta}{1 \mp \tan\theta \tan\beta}$$

Half-Angle and Double-Angle Formulas

$$\sin\frac{\theta}{2} = \pm\sqrt{\frac{1 - \cos\theta}{2}}$$

$$\cos\frac{\theta}{2} = \pm\sqrt{\frac{1 + \cos\theta}{2}}$$

$$\tan\frac{\theta}{2} = \pm\sqrt{\frac{1 - \cos\theta}{1 + \cos\theta}} = \frac{1 - \cos\theta}{\sin\theta}$$

$$= \frac{\sin\theta}{1 + \cos\theta}$$

$$\sin 2\theta = 2\sin\theta \cos\theta$$

$$\cos 2\theta = \cos^2\theta - \sin^2\theta = 1 - 2\sin^2\theta = 2\cos^2\theta - 1$$

$$\tan 2\theta = \frac{2\tan\theta}{1 - \tan^2\theta}$$

Solution of Oblique triangles

An oblique triangle is one that is not a right triangle. All the sides or all the angles of a triangle may be determined if :
1. Two angles are and a side is given.
2. Two sides and angle opposite one of them are given.
3. The included angle and two sides are given.
4. All three sides are given.

The solution is obtained using one of the two Laws given below.

Law of Cosines   This states that in any triangle ABC (see Figure below), the square of any side is equal to the sum of the other two sides minus twice the product of these sides and the cosine of the angle included by them.

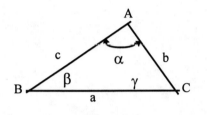

That is $a^2 = b^2 + c^2 - 2bc \cos \alpha$

Law of Sines   This states that in any triangle, the lengths of the sides are proportional to the sines of the opposite angles.

That is $\dfrac{a}{\sin \alpha} = \dfrac{b}{\sin \beta} = \dfrac{c}{\sin \gamma}$

APPENDIX C - GEOMETRY REVIEW

AREA AND VOLUMES OF VARIOUS
GEOMETRIC SHAPES

PLANE SURFACES

Notation A = area and V = volume

Rhombus

$A = bh = b^2 \sin \theta$

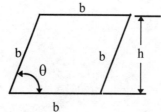

Trapezoid

$$A = \frac{h(a + b)}{2}$$

Triangle

$$A = \frac{bh}{2}$$

Circle
   r = D/2
   $A = \pi r^2 = \pi D^2/4$

Area of a sector ABC

$$A = \frac{\pi r^2 \theta^o}{360^o}$$

Area of a segment of a circle (Shaded portion)

A = area of sector ABC - area of triangle ABC

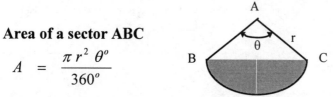

$$= \frac{r^2}{2}\left(\frac{\pi \theta^o}{180^o} - \sin \theta\right)$$

SOLIDS

Notation A = lateral area, S = surface area, and V = volume.

Rectangular parallelepiped

S = 2(ab + bh + ah)

V = abh

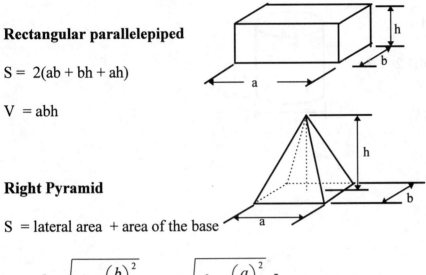

Right Pyramid

S = lateral area + area of the base

$$= \left[a\sqrt{h^2 + \left(\frac{b}{2}\right)^2} + b\sqrt{h^2 + \left(\frac{a}{2}\right)^2} \right] + ab$$

$$V = \frac{abh}{3}$$

Frustum of a right pyramid

S = lateral area + area of bottom + area of base

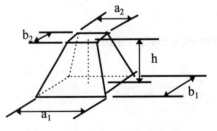

$$= (a_1 + a_2)\sqrt{h^2 + \left(\frac{b_1 - b_2}{2}\right)^2} + (b_2 + b_1)\sqrt{h^2 + \left(\frac{a_1 - a_2}{2}\right)^2} + a_1 b_1 + a_2 b_2$$

$$V = \frac{h}{3}\left(a_1 b_1 + a_2 b_2 + \sqrt{a_1 a_2 b_1 b_2}\right)$$

Right circular cylinder

$A = \pi Dh : \quad S = \pi D(D/2 + h)$

$S = \dfrac{\pi D}{2}(D + 2h)$

$V = \dfrac{\pi D^2}{4}$

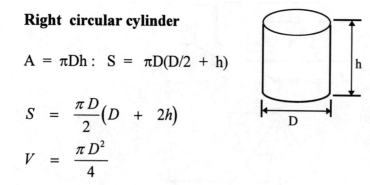

Circular right cone

$A = \dfrac{\pi DL}{2}$

$S = \dfrac{\pi D}{4}(D + 2L)$

$V = \dfrac{\pi D^2 h}{12}$

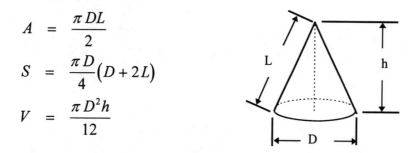

Frustum of a right cone

$A = \dfrac{\pi L}{2}(D_1 + D_2)$

$S = \dfrac{\pi}{4}\left[D_1^2 + 2L(D_1 + D_2) + D_2^2\right]$

$V = \dfrac{\pi h}{12}\left(D_1^2 + D_1 D_2 + D_2^2\right)$

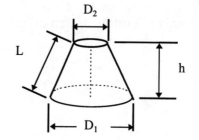

Sphere

$S = \pi D^2$

$V = \dfrac{\pi D^3}{6}$

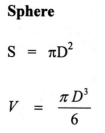
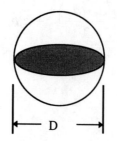

Spherical sector

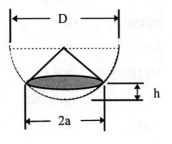

$$S = \frac{\pi D}{2}(2h + a)$$

$$V = \frac{\pi D^2 h}{6}$$

APPENDIX D - QUICK BASIC RESERVED WORDS

ABS	COMMAND$	EOF	IOCTL
ACCESS	COMMON	EQV	IOCTL$
ALIAS	CONST	ERASE	IS
AND	COS	ERDEV	KEY
ANY	CSGN	ERDEV$	KILL
APPEND	CSRLIN	ERL	LBOUND
AS	CVD	ERR	LCASE$
ASC	CVDMBF	ERROR	LEFT$
ATN	CVI	EXIT	LEN
BASE	CVL	EXP	LET
BEEP	CVS	FIELD	LINE
BINARY	CVSMBF	FILEATTR	LIST
BLOAD	DATA	FILES	LOC
BSAVE	DATE$	FIX	LOCAL
BYVAL	DECLARE	FOR	LOCATE
CALL	DEF	FRE	LOCK
CALLS	DEFDBL	FREEFILE	LOF
CASE	DEFINT	FUNCTION	LOG
CDBL	DEFLNG	GET	LONG
CDECL	DEFSNG	GOSUB	LOOP
CHAIN	DEFSTR	GOTO	LOPS
CHDIR	DIM	HEX$	LPRINT
CHR$	DO	IF	LSET
CINT	DOUBLE	IMP	LTRIM$
CIRCLE	DRAW	INKEY$	MID$
CLEAR	ELSE	INP	MKD$
CLNG	ELSEIF	INPUT	MKDIR
CLOSE	END	INPUT$	MKDMBF$
CLS	ENDIF	INSTR	MKI$
COLOR	ENVIRON	INT	MKL$
COM	ENVIRON$	INTEGER	MKS$

BASIC RESERVED WORDS (CON'T)

MKSMBF$	PRINT	SGN	THEN
MOD	PSET	SHARED	TIME$
NAME	PUT	SHELL	TIMER
NEXT	RANDOM	SIGNAL	TO
NOT	RANDOMIZE	SIN	TROFF
OCT$	READ	SINGLE	TRON
OFF	REDMIN	SLEEP	TYPE
ON	REM	SOUND	UNBOUND
OPEN	RESET	SPACE$	UCASE$
OPTION	RESTORE	SPC	UNLOCK
OR	RESUME	SQR	UNTIL
OUT	RETURN	STATIC	USING
OUTPUT	RIGHT$	STEP	VAL
PAINT	RMDIR	STICK	VARPTR
PALETTE	RND	STOP	VARPTR$
PCOPY	RSET	STR$	VARSEG
PEEK	RTRIM$	STRIG	VIEW
PEN	RUN	STRING	WAIT
PLAY	SADD	STRING$	WEND
PMAP	SCREEN	SUB	WHILE
POINT	SEEK	SWAP	WIDTH
POKE	SEG	SYSTEM	WINDOW
POS	SELECT	TAB	WRITE
PRESET	SETMEM	TAN	XOR

APPENDIX E- GENERAL INFORMATION

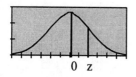

0 z

AREAS UNDER THE STANDARD
NORMAL CURVE FROM 0 TO Z

z	.00	.01	.02	.03	.04	.05	.06	.07	.08	.09
0.0	.0000	.0040	.0080	.0120	.0160	.0199	.0239	.0279	.0319	.0359
0.1	.0398	.0438	.0478	.0517	.0557	.0596	.0636	.0675	.0714	.0753
0.2	.0793	.0832	.0871	.0910	.0948	.0987	.1026	.1064	.1103	.1141
0.3	.1179	.1217	.1255	.1293	.1331	.1368	.1406	.1443	.1480	.1517
0.4	.1554	.1591	.1628	.1664	.1700	.1736	.1772	.1808	.1844	.1879
0.5	.1915	.1950	.1985	.2019	.2054	.2088	.2123	.2157	.2190	.2224
0.6	.2257	.2291	.2324	.2357	.2389	.2422	.2454	.2486	.2518	.2549
0.7	.2580	.2612	.2642	.2673	.2704	.2734	.2764	.2794	.2823	.2852
0.8	.2881	.2910	.2939	.2967	.2995	.3023	.3051	.3078	.3106	.3133
0.9	.3159	.3186	.3212	.3238	.3264	.3289	.3315	.3340	.3365	.3389
1.0	.3413	.3438	.3461	.3485	.3508	.3531	.3554	.3577	.3599	.3621
1.1	.3643	.3665	.3686	.3708	.3729	.3749	.3770	.3790	.3810	.3830
1.2	.3849	.3869	.3888	.3907	.3925	.3944	.3962	.3980	.3997	.4015
1.3	.4032	.4049	.4066	.4082	.4099	.4115	.4131	.4147	.4162	.4177
1.4	.4192	.4207	.4222	.4236	4251	.4265	.4279	.4292	.4306	.4319
1.5	.4332	.4345	.4357	.4370	.4382	.4394	.4406	.4418	.4429	.4441
1.6	.4452	.4463	.4474	.4484	.4495	.4505	.4515	.4525	.4535	.4545
1.7	.4554	.4564	.4573	.4582	.4591	.4599	.4608	.4616	.4625	.4633
1.8	.4641	.4649	.4656	.4664	.4671	.4678	.4686	.4693	.4699	.4706
1.9	.4713	.4719	.4726	.4732	.4738	.4744	.4750	.4756	.4761	.4767
2.0	.4772	.4778	.4783	.4788	.4793	.4798	.4803	.4808	.4812	.4817
2.1	.4821	.4826	.4830	.4834	4838	.4842	.4846	.4850	.4854	.4857
2.2	.4861	.4864	.4868	.4871	.4875	.4878	.4881	.4884	.4887	.4890
2.3	.4893	.4896	.4898	.4901	.4904	.4906	.4909	.4911	.4913	.4916
2.4	.4918	.4920	.4922	.4925	.4927	.4929	.4931	.4932	.4934	.4936
2.5	.4938	.4940	.4941	.4943	.4945	.4946	.4948	.4949	.4951	.4952
2.6	.4953	.4955	.4956	.4957	.4959	.4960	.4961	.4962	.4963	.4964
2.7	.4965	.4966	.4967	.4968	.4969	.4970	.4971	.4972	.4973	.4974
2.8	.4974	.4975	.4976	.4977	.4977	.4978	.4979	.4979	.4980	.4981
2.9	.4981	.4982	.4982	.4983	.4984	.4984	.4985	.4985	.4986	.4986

AREAS UNDER THE STANDARD
NORMAL CURVE FROM 0 TO Z

z	.00	.01	.02	.03	.04	.05	.06	.07	.08	.09
3.0	.4987	.4987	.4987	.4988	.4988	.4989	.4989	.4989	.4990	.4990
3.1	.4990	.4991	.4991	.4991	.4992	.4992	.4992	.4992	.4993	.4993
3.2	.4993	.4993	.4994	.4994	.4994	.4994	.4994	.4995	.4995	.4995
3.3	.4995	.4995	.4995	.4996	.4996	.4996	.4996	.4996	.4996	.4997
3.4	.4997	.4997	.4997	.4997	.4997	.4997	.4997	.4997	.4997	.4998
3.5	.4998	.4998	.4998	.4998	.4998	.4998	.4998	.4998	.4998	.4998
3.6	.4998	.4998	.4999	.4999	.4999	.4999	.4999	.4999	.4999	.4999
3.7	.4999	.4999	.4999	.4999	.4999	.4999	.4999	.4999	.4999	.4999
3.8	.4999	.4999	.4999	.4999	.4999	.4999	.4999	.4999	.4999	.4999
3.9	.5000	.5000	.5000	.5000	.5000	.5000	.5000	.5000	.5000	.5000

Physical Constants

Avogadro's number $= 6.022\ 57 \times 10^{23}$

Density of dry air at $0^{\circ}C$, 1 atm. $= 1.293$ kg/m^3

Density of water at $3.98^{\circ}C$ $= 9.999\ 973 \times 10^{2}$ kg/m^3

Equatorial radius of the earth $= 6\ 378.39$ km (3 963.34 mi)

Gravitational acceleration at sea level $= 9.806\ 65$ m/s^2

$$(32.174\ \text{ft/s}^2)$$

Heat of vaporization of water at $100^{\circ}C = 2.259\ 1 \times 10^{6}$ J/kg

Mean density of the earth $= 5.522 \times 10^{3}$ kg/m^3

$$(344.7\ \text{lbm/ft}^3)$$

Velocity of light in a vacuum $= 2.997\ 9 \times 10^{8}$ m/s

Velocity of sound in dry air at $0^{\circ}C = 331.36$ m/s $= 1\ 0871$ ft/s

APPENDIX F
Golden Section Program

```
DECLARE FUNCTION objective! (x!)
'*********************************************
'* This program uses Golden section method      *
'* to find the minimum of a given function      *
'*********************************************
'
'-------------------------------------------
'Define the bounds of the search variable
'-------------------------------------------
INPUT "What is the lower bound"; blower
INPUT "What is the upper bound"; bupper
    xlower = bupper - interv * r
    xupper = blower + interv * r
    lfun = objective(xlower)
    ufun = objective(xupper)
    test = 0
DO UNTIL test = 1
'-------------------------------------------
' A print statement can be inserted
' here if intermediate results are
' desired.
'-------------------------------------------
    IF (lfun <= ufun) THEN
'-------------------------------------------
'  Discard the region to the right
'  of xupper
'-------------------------------------------
        bupper = xupper
        xupper = xlower
        interv = bupper - blower
        xlower = bupper - interv * r
        ufun = lfun
        lfun = objective(xlower)
    ELSE
'-------------------------------------------
' Discard the region to the left of
'  xlower
'-------------------------------------------
        blower = xlower
        xlower = xupper
        interv = bupper - blower
        xupper = blower + interv * r
        lfun = ufun
        ufun = objective(xupper)
    END IF
        iter = iter + 1
    IF interv <= tol THEN
        test = 1
    END IF
LOOP
'-------------------------------------------
```

```
' final solution
' ----------------------------------------
      x1 = xlower: x2 = xupper
' ----------------------------------------
' Define the bigger of the two
' ----------------------------------------
        IF x1 > x2 THEN
            xmax = x1
        ELSE
            xmax = x2
        END IF
      fopt = objective(xmax)
PRINT "Max. value of variable=:"
    PRINT  xmax; "fopt="; fopt
END


FUNCTION objective (x)
  pi = 22 / 7: l = 9
   a = .283 * pi * x ^ 2 * l / 4
objective = a * (EXP(-x) + COS(pi * x))
END FUNCTION
```

NOTES

ANSWERS TO SELECTED PROBLEMS

CHAPTER 4

4.1 (a) 2 (c) 1 (e) 4
4.3 (a) 1 211.80 (b) 53.972
4.5 817.26 kg
4.7 121 N
4.9 $393.45
4.11 $Q = 14.59 \text{ m}^3/\text{s}$
4.13 $W = 4.20$ kN

CHAPTER 6

6.7 $d = 19.2$ km, $\theta = 51.3^\circ$
6.9 $F = 12.53$ kN, $\theta = 142.8^\circ$
6.11 $M_A = 117$ N·m (clockwise)
6.13 $T_1 = 785.04$ N, $T_2 = 1\,914.7$ N
6.15 $B_y = 293.71$ N ↑, $B_x = 700$ N ←, $A_y = 288.7$ N ↑
6.17 $\theta = 30.1^\circ$, $F = 500$ N, $A_y = 263.1$ N ↑
6.19 $F_{AB} = 4.50$ kN (T), $F_{CD} = 6.70$ kN (C)
    $F_{BD} = 6.30$ kN (C)
6.21 (a) $d = 24$ mm (c) 0.172 mm
6.23 12.74 MPa

CHAPTER 7

7.1 (a) 8 mA 9b) 0.32 W
7.3 $P = 28.8$ W, $R = 4.6\ \Omega$
7.5 (a) $16\ \Omega$ (c) 2 W
7.7 $10.54\ \Omega$
7.9 $40\ \Omega$
7.11 $I_6 = 0.23$ A

CHAPTER 8

8.1 (a) 0.625 m/s (b) 0.005 m^3/s
8.3 6.57 m/s
8.5 8.83 kJ
8.7 70 kJ, heat removed.
8.9 950 kJ, heat transferred into the system
8.11 37.4%
8.13 -9.8°C

CHAPTER 10

10.1   (a) 7.5%   (b) 12.5%
10.5   mean = 44.606, standard deviation = 0.511
10.7   81 rods
10.9   a = - 33143: b = 74.5220

CHAPTER 11

11.1 Max. value of function = 8.6336
11.3 y_{max} = 1.394
11.5   180 000 m^2

CHAPTE 12

12.1 (a) Sum = $20 865.00   (c) sum = $21 727.89
12.3 $17 301
12.5 Second option
12.7 Option b for a difference of $388.20
12.9 Reject because monthly payment ($116.24)> take home
      ($100)
12.13 difference = $129 414.80
12.15 Accept second offer ($27 025 > $25 667)
12.17 Buy machine 2
12.23 $347.97
12.25 Book value = $ 65 943

INDEX

F

G

H

W

Y

NOTES